Teaching and Learning Mathematics 11–16

Over the last five years the teaching of mathematics in secondary schools has undergone major changes. The initial and in-service education of mathematics teachers has also changed almost beyond recognition. *Teaching and Learning Mathematics* examines the effects of these changes, from the introduction of the National Curriculum and GCSE, to developments such as individualised learning, investigations, and microcomputers. It surveys the content of secondary school mathematics, comparing the demands of the National Curriculum with research evidence about children's learning, and explores approaches to teaching the subject within the wider curriculum.

Drawing upon the author's own classroom experience and upon the latest research findings, the book provides plenty of practical advice on effective teaching and organisational strategies. It explores issues of classroom management and approaches to teaching the subject within the wider curriculum. It discusses the important social issues of teaching, such as multicultural education, gender, and the provision for children with special educational needs, and shows how they are related to the concerns of the mathematics teacher. This book provides a comprehensive text for mathematics teachers at every stage in their professional development.

John Costello is Lecturer in Education (Mathematics) at Loughborough University. He also works with teachers and students in schools, and was involved in compiling a review of research in mathematics education.

Teaching and Learning Mathematics 11–16

John Costello

ROUTLEDGE

London and New York

First published 1991
by Routledge
11 New Fetter Lane, London EC4P 4EE

Simultaneously published in the USA and Canada
by Routledge
a division of Routledge, Chapman and Hall, Inc.
29 West 35th Street, New York, NY 10001

Typeset by Gilfillan Ltd.
65 Mortimer Road, Mitcham, Surrey

Printed in Great Britain by
Mackays of Chatham PLC, Chatham, Kent

British Library Cataloguing in Publication Data
Costello, John *1945-*
Teaching and learning mathematics 11-16
1. Great Britain. Secondary schools. Curriculum
Mathematics
I. Title
510.71241

ISBN 0-415-05832-5
ISBN 0-415-04988-1 pbk

Library of Congress Cataloguing-in-Publication Data
Has been applied for

Contents

Preface

This book presents an overview of the teaching and learning of mathematics in secondary schools. It draws upon classroom experience and research findings to describe how mathematics can be taught and learnt within the context of the National Curriculum, and explores the issues which are likely to be seen as important in this context. It is intended to provide a starting point for students or newly qualified teachers of mathematics, as well as an opportunity for more experienced teachers to review the current situation. Each section suggests books, articles and other sources for those who wish to study particular issues in greater depth.

Some short excerpts from previously published material are included by agreement. Acknowledgments are due to the National Curriculum Council for the statements of attainment and associated illustrative examples, and to the Assessment of Performance Unit for test data and for the assessment framework in Chapter 1. Kathleen Hart has kindly allowed me to include some material from the Concepts in Secondary Mathematics and Science, Strategies and Errors in Secondary Mathematics and Children's Mathematical Frameworks research: some of this appeared originally in *Mathematics in School*, and is quoted by permission of the editors. Also I should like to thank Louis Cohen for some of the ideas in Chapter 8, Susan Pirie for a lot of the work on investigations, Keith Selkirk for an idea in Chapter 9, and Rita Nolder for case study material quoted in Chapters 8, 9 and 10.

A book which attempts to give a balanced picture of teaching mathematics must inevitably incorporate the views and suggestions of a large number of people. Sources are quoted throughout the text, and I have tried to represent people's ideas as faithfully and sensitively as I can. The responsibility for any errors or misrepresentation in this matter is of course entirely mine.

JOHN COSTELLO

Chapter 1

The nature of school mathematics and the National Curriculum

MATHEMATICAL LEARNING

Any discussion of the nature of school mathematics can be conducted at a number of different levels. Ostensibly, mathematics is about number, shape, algebra, measurement and a variety of other more specialised but nevertheless familiar topics which give the subject its particular flavour. By and large these topics are recognisable as mathematics, although they have applications or echoes in other areas of study.

On the other hand, while the subject content of school mathematics is identifiable and distinctive, it is much less clear that it demands specific forms of learning or even ability. If it is possible to pinpoint different types of learning, then these are likely to exist across a range of different school subjects. For example, learning mathematics involves some memory capacity – the ability to acquire and retain knowledge. Yet, while remembering knowledge has some part to play, it may be a very limited aspect of learning mathematics compared with other subject areas. In contrast, if we want to identify a form of learned attainment more characteristic of mathematics in particular, we might try to define 'problem-solving' ability – the kind of insight into a problem which provides a strategy leading to its solution. Again, this could be part of any curriculum area, but most people would probably associate problem solving with mathematics more than with other school subjects. Attempts to describe and classify the kinds of learning involved in mathematics have been going on for a long time: a discussion and synopsis of these is provided by Brown (in Floyd 1978). Typically, these schemes distinguish the learning of facts, skills, conceptual structures, problem-solving strategies and attitudes. However simplistic this model of mathematical learning might be, it enables us at least to begin to clarify what otherwise appears as a somewhat amorphous collection of activities. Such tentative taxonomies have influenced research and curriculum development in mathematics in recent years in a number of ways. The large-scale surveys of the Assessment of Performance Unit (APU) from 1978 to 1982 were based on a similar classification. The Cockcroft Committee adopted the same theme in developing recommendations on teaching methods which led to the most frequently quoted section of the Cockcroft Report (1982), concerned with classroom practice. Most recently, these ideas have fed through, in a modified form, into the attainment targets and programmes of study for mathematics in the National Curriculum. Given the widespread use of such classifications, it is worth pausing for a little while to re-examine the categories and consider what they are and how useful they have been.

Facts are items of knowledge – pieces of information which are known and remembered. It is often claimed that isolated, arbitrary knowledge of this kind has very little place in mathematics learning. It might indeed be that disconnected facts play only a very small part in any human learning: most of what we know is embedded in rich structures and memories. On the other hand, regardless of the complexity surrounding it, a lot of knowledge is available to us by immediate recall. There are plenty of questions to which we can respond correctly without worrying about what they mean. It is perhaps easier to recognise this outside mathematics: if asked, for example, 'What is the capital of Ecuador?', most people will produce the answer 'Quito' (if they produce it at all) by immediate recall without consideration of the meaning of the question, why it has been asked or how this knowledge could be useful. If there is then an opportunity to reflect on the question and answer, some people might imagine the size and shape of Ecuador, envisage mentally a map of South America, or, if they have any connection with that part of the world, remember a personal experience. Yet, in spite of these contextual features, the original answer is most probably produced as a quick response triggered by the wording of the question, in the style and tradition of a television quiz programme.

Is there any knowledge in mathematics like this? Well, for most people, yes, quite a bit. Consider the multiplication question 7 x 6 = ?, or, in words, 'what are seven sixes?' According to many authorities, including the Cockcroft Report, such so-called number facts do not fit into this category, because they are not unconnected or arbitrary but follow logically from an understanding of the number system. So they do, but it remains true that most people recall the answer 42 without recourse to their understanding of that system. If some explanation or justification or application of the knowledge is demanded, then structural understanding needs to be evoked; but the bare answer has become available, detached from that structure. To try to describe this condition, we resort to metaphors: you might say that the answer is on the tip of your tongue or at the front of your mind. Knowledge is likely to stay in this position if it is required and recalled regularly. It may have been learned by rote or by frequent usage, but the form in which it was originally acquired seems to make little difference to its availability. Many people respond correctly to the question 'seven plus six' (7 + 6 = ?) in exactly the same way, even though addition facts are most unlikely to have been taught in the same planned way as the multiplication tables.

Reflection on just how the question triggers the response can also provide some insight into the different ways in which memory operates. What precisely made you think '42'? Was it the appearance of the symbols '7 x 6', or the sound (spoken, mouthed or rehearsed internally) of the words 'seven sixes'? The following geometrical example, in which a word has to be identified, provides another illustration.

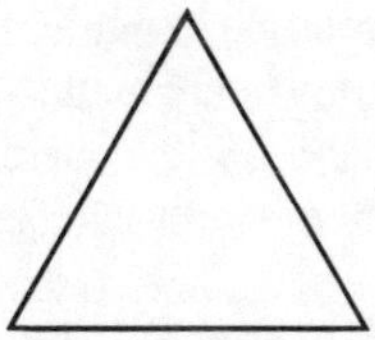

What do we call a triangle like this, with all three sides equal?

Here the fact to be recalled is a technical term, an item of mathematical language. It is debatable just how much specialist language of this kind is important and useful in school mathematics, and this issue is discussed in Chapter 17. The particular word 'equilateral', however, is well known, and most people are able to decide whether it is the picture or the phrase 'all three sides equal' which most brings the word to mind.

There are lots of other mathematical devices which are commonly remembered in isolation, including a variety of formulae, like $2\pi r$ and πr^2. Yet it is the names, symbols, conventions and terminology of mathematics which provide the most arbitrary examples. The definitions of sine, cosine and tangent in terms of the angles and sides of a right-angled triangle, for instance, form a structure with some internal consistency, but seem very arbitrary. This makes them difficult to remember, so that various mnemonics are invented – artificial aids to memory which more thoughtful teachers are inclined to regard with considerable unease. In reality, of course, nothing is entirely arbitrary; but the context which justifies the meaning of terms like 'equilateral' or 'sine, cosine and tangent' is linguistic and historical rather than mathematical, and for that reason, while no doubt interesting, is less likely to be considered worthy of investigation or explanation.

Factual recall, while sometimes impressive, is of no great value without a context in which it can be understood and used. You may or may not know the value of $\sqrt{5}$ to three decimal places (2.236), but in itself this knowledge is less important than other issues which surround it. What does $\sqrt{5}$ mean? Can you convince someone else of the accuracy of the approximation 2.236? Can you use this knowledge sensibly in solving a problem? If you have this contextual competence, it does not matter very much whether you can remember the actual value; and if you haven't, it matters even less.

Skills are standard, well-established procedures, which are used in more or less the same format again and again. There is a popular view that learning mathematics is essentially about developing skills and that such procedures are the foundation of mathematical competence. It is an idea which is reinforced by the use of the expression 'basic skills' by politicians and in the media. Yet it is a narrow and unrealistic perception of mathematics as it is practised and applied in everyday life, in employment and in academic study. It is a perception which has been repeatedly challenged, by research and by curriculum developments in schools, over a long period. Indeed, it is arguable that many curriculum developments viewed as radical in their time, such as the 'modern mathematics' projects of the 1960s and the growth of 'investigations' in the 1980s, were motivated partly by the desire to counterbalance an excessive emphasis on routine skills.

The word 'algorithm' has come to be used to describe any routine, well-defined mathematical procedure. Most often it refers to a method for carrying out a specific arithmetical calculation, but it may equally well be applied to a procedure for solving a particular type of algebraic equation, for constructing a geometrical figure or for carrying out an accurate measurement or a statistical test. Traditionally, algorithms are most often regarded as pencil-and-paper methods, but in recent years awareness has grown of the importance of established mental procedures and of calculator and computer techniques. It is also a mistake to assume that mathematical skills are necessarily taught, learnt and practised in some standard form: individuals commonly develop their own, sometimes idiosyncratic, algorithms which are then used regularly, often with some success.

Like factual recall, the ability to perform a skill is of little practical use without the awareness of its purpose and meaning which provides understanding of the contexts in which it may be applied appropriately. It is sometimes claimed that the mastery of a standard technique is itself motivating, and that pupils enjoy the sense of competence acquired by the successful repetition of a procedure. Such satisfaction, while no doubt real, is essentially limited, however; and the kind of competence needed in mathematics is functional in terms of its application and interpretation.

All this discussion leads to the view that an understanding of *conceptual structures* is necessary to give meaning and value to mathematical knowledge and skills. Such structures involve interconnecting relationships and properties. Consider this task:

> Cheese is priced at £2.65 per kilogram. How much will a block weighing 0.38 kg cost?

Before the appropriate calculation can be performed, the question demands sufficient understanding of arithmetical operations to make this recognisable as a multiplication task. It may be clear that the task requires some calculation with the numbers 2.65 and 0.38, but what? A geometrical example is provided by the first APU survey of primary mathematics (APU 1985), which includes the following item:

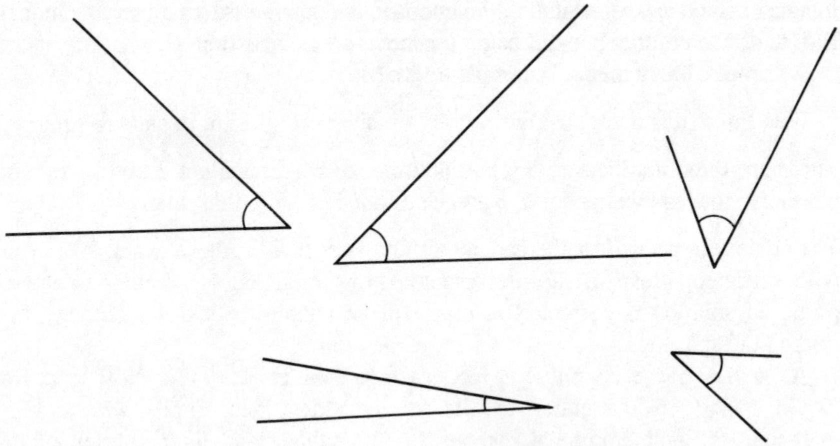

Put a ring round the angle which is a different size from all the others

The growth in understanding concepts, such as 'multiplication' and 'angle size' in these examples, involves both the accumulation of experience and the elimination of irrelevant features of situations. In promoting this growth, variety is important in the models and situations provided. For instance, if subtraction is always described as, and illustrated by, 'taking away', this operation will not become recognisable in the whole range of situations in which it is relevant; and it will not extend easily, for example, to negative numbers.

The angle example above requires the abstraction of a specific feature, the size of the angles. 76 per cent of 11-year-old children tested were able to complete the task successfully: most of those who did not do so were distracted either by the short arms of one figure or the unequal arms of another.

Characteristically, mathematical activity demands the ability to devise *strategies* for solving problems. An example is the following:

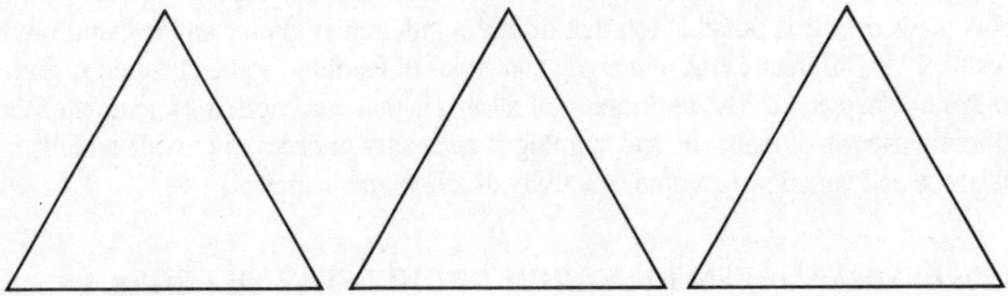

How can you cut up and rearrange three equilateral triangles to make one single equilateral triangle?

The strategic element of this question is an inventive step. It is quite possible to imagine someone understanding the question and having the necessary technical skill to do the cutting, but still being unable to do the question.

A comparable numerical example might be:

Find three (different, positive, whole) numbers which sum in pairs to squares.

There are three numbers a, b, c, so that $a + b$, $a + c$ and $b + c$ are all square numbers: how can values for a, b and c be found?

The creative aspect of mathematical activity is critical in these examples. Even with sufficient grasp of the problem to know immediately whether or not a proposed solution is correct, you may still be unable to devise a strategy for finding the solution.

As well as these cognitive aspects of mathematical learning, most teachers would want to pay attention to affective considerations. Pupils' *attitudes* to mathematics, their emotional response to the subject and their opinion of its nature and purpose, may be considered important objectives in their own right, and they certainly affect pupils' motivation. These matters are dealt with in some detail in Chapter 13.

The distinctions identified here between different forms of mathematical activity relate very much to the competence possessed by an individual. The example quoted of providing an approximate value for $\sqrt{5}$ may be a matter of factual recall for one person, but for another it might involve a combination of skill, understanding and strategy. Similarly, a category of problem which demands the invention of a strategy when it is first encountered may become the application of a routine skill with regular usage. For these reasons, it is often not sensible to assign tasks and test items in themselves to such categories.

Perhaps more significant than the classifications of particular questions are the balance and presentation of the mathematics curriculum and the relative emphasis which is given to different forms of learning. Thus, a syllabus or scheme of work may be designed or expressed in a way which leads to concentration on routine skills, or on understanding structure, or on devising strategies for solving problems. Also, an individual teacher may, consciously or otherwise, adopt a teaching approach which emphasises a particular aspect of mathematical learning at the expense of other forms of competence. It is possible too that different pupils may prefer and respond more positively to different forms of activity and styles of learning; some attention is given to this in Chapter 12. The implication of all this is that a conscious awareness of the different aspects of mathematical learning is necessary in order to provide a realistic, balanced and varied programme of activity in school mathematics.

THE CSMS AND SESM RESEARCH AT CHELSEA COLLEGE

The two decades from 1970 to 1990 saw a massive expansion of research activity in mathematical education. Much of this research is the work of individuals and on a small scale; some has been reported in the journal *Educational Studies in Mathematics*, or, particularly when it has been considered important to disseminate the classroom implications, in *Mathematics Teaching* or *Mathematics in School*. Reviews of research have been published during this period, for example those by Bell *et al.* (1983) and Dickson *et al.* (1984); but, at a time when this research field is popular, such reviews quickly become dated, and an up-to-date, comprehensive anthology of research cannot easily be provided.

Amongst this research activity, however, the work at Chelsea College has been exceptional. The mathematics findings of the Concepts in Secondary Mathematics and Science (CSMS) programme were well publicised in books and in articles in a variety of publications. The project was funded for the years 1974–9, and the research was firmly based in schools and on the school curriculum, providing a detailed overview of the level of competence of secondary school children in the mathematical topics commonly taught to that age group. The results are described in a book by Hart (1981).

Obviously, a substantial project of this nature has its effects on developments for quite a number of years. The results suggest directions for curriculum change, for the development of teaching approaches, and for further research. As a sequel to CSMS the Strategies and Errors in Secondary Mathematics (SESM) project, during 1980–3, investigated in some depth the difficulties experienced and strategies commonly used by secondary school pupils. One feature of the CSMS results is the high incidence of certain wrong answers, frequently obtained by the established use of inappropriate strategies. The SESM work identified these, and also investigated whether and to what extent pupils' performance in such circumstances might be improved by specially designed teaching programmes.

A lot of the detail of the CSMS project in particular continues to provide useful information for analysis, discussion and further development. Furthermore the treatment of some topic areas has provided a framework within which strategies for teaching, learning and doing mathematics can be described and interpreted. Chapter 3, on algebra, in this book uses an example of such a framework.

There are also a number of more general conclusions which have emerged gradually from analysis of the CSMS results and from later development based on these. One is the extent to which pupils use strategies and procedures which they have not been taught, sometimes appropriately and sometimes not, in tackling mathematical questions. This has become a fertile and often entertaining field for research. Another broad effect has been an increased awareness of just how difficult school mathematics is for some pupils and of the enormous variation in attainment amongst pupils of the same age. This awareness has had its repercussions in the format of new textbooks and schemes, in the development of the GCSE examination, and in the association of levels of attainment in the National Curriculum with specific ages.

THE APU SURVEYS

The APU was set up within the Department of Education and Science in 1975. Its intention was to provide information about general levels of performance of pupils in school and how these change over the years. The APU mathematics team began work in 1977 with a brief to carry out the first surveys of 11 and 15 year olds the following year. These 1978 surveys became the first in a series of five annual surveys at each level which was completed in 1982. Results from the first three surveys at 11 and 15 were published in six separate detailed reports, but the findings of the later surveys appeared in a piecemeal way in a number of articles. A comprehensive description of all ten surveys is, however, available in an updated two-volume report *A Review of Monitoring in Mathematics 1978 to 1982* which was produced later in the 1980s (APU 1985).

The APU mathematics surveys adopted an assessment framework based on a two-way classification of items by content and by 'learning outcome'. The five main content categories, number, measures, geometry, algebra, and probability and statistics, are almost identical with those which have subsequently been used to define the attainment targets in the National Curriculum. In the first primary and secondary reports, the terms 'concept', 'skill' and 'application' were used to describe categories of learning outcome. Thus, the item about angle size quoted earlier in this chapter tests a 'concept' in geometry. This example is relatively clear-cut, but others are less so. Outcomes classified in this way seem better defined in relation to number than the other content areas, but even in number there are difficulties. How, for example, should the item about the cost of 0.38 kg of cheese be classified? Does it test awareness of the concept of multiplication by demanding its recognition in a situation, or is it an application? The APU review recognises the weakness of the applications category, explaining that some so-called applications are little more than routine exercises involving one operation, while others demand complex applications of a mathematical model.

Considerations of this nature led to some development of the assessment framework over the years; the two-way classification adopted in the later reports is summarised in Table 1.

In some areas, the detailed APU data can be compared with the findings of the CSMS research. Some such comparisons are made in the APU review itself, for example in the chapter on algebra. Interestingly, a great deal of common ground can be identified between the results of the two programmes, even though they appear initially to be quite different in nature and motivation. In his foreword to Hart's book (1981), Matthews describes the CSMS work as 'finding just what secondary children are capable of learning, and where they are in their development'. To this extent, the project had its roots in cognitive psychology: it developed from a consideration of how the earlier Nuffield Mathematics Project was able to develop a hierarchy of concepts, based on a Piagetian theory of development. In contrast, the APU has been very much concerned with monitoring standards in schools, and its early publicity material in particular

Table 1

	Outcome			
	Concepts and skills		Problem-solving	Attitudes
Content	Age 11	Age 15	strategies	
Number	Concepts: whole numbers; decimals and fractions Computation: whole numbers and decimals; fractions Applications Rate and ratio	Concepts Skills Applications	Investigations/creativity: Processing information Formulating problems Strategies and methods of solution Generalising solutions Proving Evaluating results	Attitudes to practical mathematics: willingness to handle apparatus; confidence; anxiety about success; verbal fluency; persistence Enjoyment, utility and difficulty of specific mathematical topics in the curriculum. Liking, difficulty and utility of mathematics as a subject
Measures	Money, time, mass, temperature Length, area, volume, capacity	Unit Rate and Ratio Mensuration		
Algebra	Generalised arithmetic Sets and relations	General Traditional Graphical Modern		
Geometry	Shapes, lines, angles Symmety, transformations, coordinates	Descriptive Modern Trigonometry		
Probability and statistics	Probability and data representation	Probability Statistics		

was expressed very much in such terms. An early APU pamphlet describing its work begins: 'Everyone wants to raise educational standards. But how do we know what the educational standards are?'

Both the CSMS results and the APU reports quote 'facilities' – the percentages of pupils able to complete test items successfully. By its very nature, the CSMS research emphasised the understanding of conceptual structures, so that comparisons which investigate pupils' awareness of properties and relationships are the most likely to produce worthwhile information.

As an illustration, one aspect of children's grasp of the place value system applied to whole numbers is tested by their ability to add or subtract one from a number at the critical stage when zero appears in the units column. The APU surveys include the following item:

The number which is one less than 2010 is....

The correct answer is obtained by 71 per cent of 11 year olds and 88 per cent of 15 year olds. Incidentally, the quoted facility for 11 year olds has been revised upwards over the years: the figure given by the first APU survey, carried out in 1978, was 64 per cent.

The CSMS tests include this question:

This meter counts the number of people going into a football stand:

0	6	3	9	9

After one more person has gone in it will read:

The facilities are

Age:	12	13	14	15
	68%	77%	86%	88%

These results are reassuringly consistent. They show that a clear majority of 11/12-year-old children have this understanding at the beginning of their secondary school years. They also give a clear indication of the size of the minority who have not achieved the understanding by the age of 15.

The APU surveys have provided an enormous amount of material, much of which has not been completely analysed or interpreted. Discussion and reappraisal of the findings has continued in articles and in a series of short reports in booklet form. Much of the work deserves further investigation and development. The construction and use of practical tests may lead to a more flexible approach to assessment in the National Curriculum. The work on attitudes and gender differences sheds some light on these difficult areas and the relationship between them: this is explored in more detail in later chapters.

THE COCKCROFT REPORT

The events which led to the Cockcroft Inquiry began with a speech by James Callaghan at Ruskin College in 1975. The ensuing 'Great Debate' involved discussions and the collection of evidence throughout the country and many contributors raised questions about the mathematical attainments of children in school. These questions concerned an alleged lack of basic computational skills, an increase in the mathematical demands made on adults, the lack of qualified mathematics teachers and a variety of other issues including communications and relationships between education and employers. As a response to this concern, the Secretary of State, Shirley Williams, set up an inquiry into the teaching of mathematics. The committee of inquiry first met in 1978, and its report was published, with the support of the new Secretary of State, Sir Keith Joseph, in 1982.

Anxiety about standards of achievement in school mathematics appears to be a permanent feature of British life. Complaints of declining standards have been made regularly in the press and by government organisations for well over a hundred years – perhaps always – and the Cockcroft Report includes a selection of such quotations. Each generation looks back to imagined higher standards, and finds a way to castigate the young, or, more often, their teachers, for their poor attainment in mathematics.

Of course there is no evidence of this long-term decline. The need to articulate such anxieties on particular occasions owes more to social and cultural factors than to the realities of mathematical attainment. The complaints of the 1970s were part of a reaction to the changes of the 1960s, which were by then being portrayed as notoriously radical. Mathematics education was just one focus of this concern, which pervaded many aspects of life. It has been typified by one commentator (see Bell *et al.* 1983) as a swing of the pendulum away from easier divorce and abortion towards higher pay for the police. Others see it (Jenkins 1989) as part of the process which produced more right wing governments in the 1980s.

In practice, it is logistically difficult to compare levels of attainment in mathematics over a period of time. There are some records available of test scores of candidates for entry to particular categories of employment, including, for example, the Navy, over an extended period: these show considerable variation, and sometimes an apparent decline. These changes, however, reflect rapid movements in the stratum of ability from which candidates are drawn – movements which follow underlying changes in economic conditions and which have little connection with standards of education.

Even if it were possible to test a sufficiently large and representative group of pupils using items administered to a similar group some years earlier, the interpretation of the results would be controversial. Over the years, the content and emphasis of the mathematics curriculum have changed – quite rightly so, since school mathematics must reflect the changes in needs and usage. A test which was appropriate some years ago would no longer reflect the mathematical experience of children now in schools, and, if it were used again, the results would inevitably seem to show a decline in performance. The first of the consultation documents for Mathematics in the National Curriculum (August 1988) quotes an illustration of this. A report by the National Foundation for Educational Research (NFER) compared the performance of a sample of 13-year-old pupils in 1981 with a sample of 13-year-old pupils in 1964 on 37 virtually identical questions. Average test scores in 1981 were significantly lower than in 1964. The consultation document points out that the style of mathematics teaching had changed since the 1960s, making some of the test items less appropriate. It is perhaps a pity that, while recognising this and many other reservations, the authors of this particular document went to some lengths to present 'evidence' of declining standards. The case is not well made, and yet its presentation encourages the sense that this is a criticism of the performance of teachers and schools in recent years and that the National Curriculum is a government initiative to remedy these deficiencies. It is easy for public opinion to latch on to this view, which is neither accurate nor particularly helpful.

As part of its work, the Cockcroft Committee set up studies into the mathematical needs of employment and of adult life, and also commissioned a review of existing research on the teaching and learning of mathematics. Using this review of research the report picks up the distinctions amongst different aspects of mathematical learning. The implications of these distinctions for effective mathematics teaching are discussed in a section which leads to the most frequently quoted recommendation of the report, paragraph 243:

> Mathematics teaching at all levels should include opportunities for:
>
> - exposition by the teacher;
> - discussion between teacher and pupils and between pupils themselves;
> - appropriate practical work;
> - consolidation and practice of fundamental skills and routines;
> - problem solving, including the application of mathematics to everyday situations;
> - investigational work.

The Cockcroft Report was very well received: the foreword by the secretaries of state describes it as a first-class report and commends it to all those concerned about the quality of mathematics taught in schools. One of its most significant achievements was to encourage rather than stifle progressive developments at a time when anxiety about standards created some pressure for a 'back-to-basics' movement. There were some who would have wished the report to indicate a definitive style for the teaching of mathematics, yet the report recognises that this is neither desirable nor possible.

The National Curriculum consultation document (1988) recognised the valuable influence of the Cockcroft Report in highlighting and disseminating good practice in schools. If, in the years since the report's publication, the development of mathematics education in schools has not been entirely satisfactory, this is not because old skills have become neglected. Far from it. If anything, it is arguable that fresh ideas have not been taken on board, and that the mathematics curriculum has not changed radically enough or quickly enough to meet the altered needs of a new generation. This is hardly surprising. When commercial considerations are allowed to prevail, economic, industrial and technological aspects of life can move relatively quickly. Schools, however, are completely dependent on staffing, accommodation and other resources, which cannot be overhauled rapidly, especially when there can be no commitment to the high level of public expenditure which drastic change demands.

In some ways the National Curriculum requirements represent an enforced change. For example, the attainment targets demand an appropriate use of calculators and computers in a range of specified activities, rather than allowing schools and teachers discretion about when or whether to make use of these devices. On the other hand, some aspects of the attainment targets are less forward-looking. The National Curriculum Council (NCC) is responsible for keeping these details under review and suggesting changes in the light of experience, and Her Majesty's Inspectorate (HMI) also monitors schools' experience of the statutory requirements. It is to be hoped that these arrangements can be used to update the curriculum in a sensible and constructive way.

MATHEMATICS IN THE NATIONAL CURRICULUM

The statutory requirements were published in a loose-leaf bound document, *Mathematics in the National Curriculum*, early in 1989. Subsequent material to be added to this publication includes the *Non-Statutory Guidance* issued in June 1989. These provisions came into force in August 1989, with immediate effect as far as 11-year-old pupils in the first year of secondary schooling were concerned, followed by a phased introduction throughout the secondary years. The NCC has introduced a new description for school year groups, covering the ages 5–18: in this system the 11–16 age-range corresponds to years 7–11 (Y7–Y11), and Y12 and Y13 are the traditional sixth-form years. It remains to be seen whether this convention will come into general usage quickly.

The National Curriculum legislation operates by prescribing 'attainment targets' – specific forms of competence which pupils are expected to achieve. These are then translated into 'programmes of study' – broadly defined classroom activities which should allow pupils to acquire the levels of learning required. In setting out the requirements for mathematics, the specification and classification of attainment targets caused some difficulty. As already explained, the tasks of school mathematics can be classified both by content area and by type of learning. Furthermore, each attainment target has to be specified at ten 'levels', representing the degree of sophistication of pupils' competence in the particular aspect of mathematics. These considerations suggest a complex, multidimensional model of learning mathematics, which in this context is quite impractical. For one thing, information about the performance of pupils and schools within the National Curriculum framework has to be published in a form accessible to parents, governing bodies, local authorities and the wider community. This communication demands a relatively simple and comprehensible format.

In the August 1988 consultation document, a working group proposed three broad 'profile components'. The first included knowledge, skills and understanding in number, algebra and measures; the second, knowledge, skills and understanding in shape and space, and handling data; and the third, entitled 'practical applications of mathematics', included a broad spectrum of practical usage, problem-solving ability, communication skills and personal qualities. It is more difficult to define and assess some aspects of this third component unambiguously, and the format of the third component proved unacceptable within the framework of the proposed legislation. In spite of strong protestations from specialist professional organisations concerned with mathematics education, the statements of attainment associated with this component were mostly removed from the requirements. Those that remain appear in a somewhat different form in two attainment targets, numbered 1 and 9.

There are fourteen attainment targets in all, organised into two main blocks, as follows:

Knowledge, skills, understanding and use of number, algebra and measures

AT1	Using and applying mathematics	Use number, algebra and measures in practical tasks, in real-life problems, and to investigate within mathematics itself.
AT2	Number	Understand number and number notation.
AT3	Number	Understand number operations (addition, subtraction, multiplication and division) and make use of appropriate methods of calculation.
AT4	Number	Estimate and approximate in number.
AT5	Number/Algebra	Recognise and use patterns, relationships and sequences, and make generalisations.
AT6	Algebra	Recognise and use functions, formulae, equations and inequalities.

AT7	Algebra	Use graphical representation of algebraic functions.
AT8	Measures	Estimate and measure quantities, and appreciate the approximate nature of measurement.

Knowledge, skills, understanding and use of shape and space and data handling

AT9	Using and applying mathematics	Use shape and space and handle data in practical tasks, in real-life problems, and to investigate within mathematics itself.
AT10	Shape and space	Recognise and use the properties of two-dimensional and three-dimensional shapes.
AT11	Shape and space	Recognise location and use transformations in the study of space.
AT12	Handling data	Collect, record and process data.
AT13	Handling data	Represent and interpret data.
AT14	Handling data	Understand, estimate and calculate probabilities.

Attainment Targets 1 and 9 are different in style from the others. They are, as it were, enabling facilities which provide the ability to make use of the knowledge and skills in AT2 – AT8 and AT10 – AT14 respectively.

All the attainment targets are to be considered relevant throughout the compulsory (5–16) years of schooling, and their demands are specified at ten different levels. Thus, for example, AT10 begins with level 1, at which pupils should be able to:

- sort three-dimensional and two-dimensional shapes;
- build with three-dimensional solid shapes and draw two-dimensional shapes and describe them.

At level 10, pupils should be able to:

- use angle and tangent properties of circles;
- sketch the graphs of sine, cosine and tangent functions for all angles;
- generate trigonometric functions using a calculator or computer and interpret them;
- use sine and cosine rules to solve problems, including simple cases in three-dimensions.

In most cases the statements of attainment are illustrated by examples which make the intention clear. The programmes of study for each level do not in general add any new information to the attainment targets, but they do present the requirements in a form which may prove more useful to schools and teachers in planning schemes of work for different classes.

In recognition of the wide range of ability in mathematics, the matching of levels of attainment to age groups allows some flexibility. The years of compulsory school are divided into four key stages: the following table shows the age range, and specified range of levels of attainment, for each key stage:

Key stage	Year	Age range	Levels
KS1	Y1 – Y2	5 – 7	1 – 3
KS2	Y3 – Y6	7 – 11	2 – 6
KS3	Y7 – Y9	11 – 14	3 – 8
KS4	Y10 – Y11	14 – 16	4 – 10

It is expected that the attainment of the great majority of pupils will fall within the specified range at the end of each key stage. Even with the amount of overlap allowed, there will no doubt be a small number of pupils whose actual attainment falls outside the range indicated; but teachers are nevertheless required to teach with a view to the achievement by pupils of levels within the appropriate, specified range. It is anticipated that most pupils will meet standards close to the middle of the ranges. Typically pupils at the reporting age of 14 will reach level 5 or 6, and by age 16 will reach about level 6 or 7. It may be noted, however, that pupils in the fourth and fifth year of secondary schools may legitimately be given work at any of the seven levels, 4 – 10.

At or near the end of each key stage, arrangements are made to assess the achievement of each pupil in each attainment target. These arrangements involve a combination of externally determined standard assessment tasks (SATs) and teachers' own assessments. The development and implementation of assessment procedures is considered in a later chapter.

The *Non-Statutory Guidance* (June 1989) provides many useful suggestions, designed to support the teaching of mathematics in the National Curriculum. The guidelines on school policy statements, schemes of work and lesson plans in mathematics are particularly important, although they do not of course represent legal requirements. In such matters, schools inevitably begin from different positions and need to adopt approaches which reflect their particular needs and priorities. There is scope for individual style, and much of the work of implementing the National Curriculum involves building on existing arrangements and structures previously established in schools.

Chapter 2

Number and numeracy

INTRODUCTION

The National Curriculum includes three attainment targets entitled 'number'. The range of activity and achievement contained in these requirements is commonly accepted as fundamental in mathematics learning. Indeed, when concern is expressed about standards it is usually focused on this area; and there are many courses and examinations, particularly of a vocational nature, which include an element called 'numeracy', sometimes concerned exclusively with competence in number. In this way numeracy has become presented as a distinct subject area, closely related to mathematics but narrower in its coverage of topics and at the same time more functional in its applicability to daily life and work.

Leaving aside for the moment any debate about the validity of this view, even if we restrict our attention to those aspects of mathematical performance concerned with number as distinct from shape and so on, there is plenty of scope for disagreement. As a starting-point it is useful to ask what competence in number involves, and just what degree of facility with number we should reasonably expect most people to achieve.

In this exercise there are two kinds of criteria which could conceivably be in conflict: the needs and demands of our society and the intellectual potential and development of our children. Both of these have at times been misunderstood. The real needs of today's world are quite different from many people's perception of them, and the wide range of children's ability in mathematics is often underestimated. However, it is possible to identify some abilities which most people would agree are useful, and even essential, aspects of numeracy. These might include the following:

- Knowledge of certain facts, so that these are available by immediate recall from memory. This body of knowledge is relatively small, but it might well include addition facts (e.g. 5 + 7 = 12) and multiplication tables, up to perhaps 10 + 10 and 10 x 10 respectively.

- An appreciation and understanding of the way in which numbers are written in place value notation, including decimal fractions. This involves, for example, being able to put numbers in order of size or to say what number is one more than 10099.

- Some procedures for carrying out arithmetical computation. These could be:

  (a) standard, taught, pencil-and-paper methods, such as

$$\begin{array}{rcc} & {}^{6}\not{7} & {}^{12}\not{2} \\ - & 2 & 9 \\ \hline & 4 & 3 \end{array} \quad \text{or} \quad \begin{array}{cc} 7 & {}^{12}\not{2} \\ {}^{3}\not{2} & 9 \\ \hline 4 & 3 \end{array}$$

  (b) individual, possibly self-devised, mental techniques, for example '29, one more makes 30, and 42 makes 72, so 72 – 29 = 43';
  (c) pressing the right buttons on a calculator.

- An understanding of what the arithmetical operations are, which

  (a) permits the recognition of the appropriate operation in a word problem or practical situation, and
  (b) provides judgment about whether an obtained answer is reasonable.

Common agreement on this subject is elusive and many people would want to modify or add to this list in some way. Nevertheless, this relatively limited collection of learning represents a basic package of number competence for everyday life.

The three number attainment targets of the National Curriculum are concerned with number notation, number operations, and estimation and approximation respectively. All parts of the mathematics curriculum are of course related and these strands of number development are especially closely interwoven so that separation into compartments can be misleading. A constructive approach is to examine the characteristics of these components and also of the connections between them.

NUMBER AND NUMBER NOTATION

Attainment Target 2 begins with the understanding and use of the words and symbols representing small numbers for counting, and progresses to larger numbers, fractions, decimals and negative numbers. At the higher levels it includes index notation, standard form, ratios and irrational numbers.

The results of the CSMS and APU work quoted in Chapter 1 indicate just how difficult some of these ideas are for many pupils, and highlight in particular the wide variation in pupils' understanding of the place–value system. In practice, weaknesses in the conceptual structure generally become apparent through pupils' behaviour when asked to perform some procedure. Thus it is attempts to put numbers in order, add or subtract one and so on which show up inadequate awareness of the structure. In the more recent Children's Mathematical Frameworks (CMF) research, Hart (1987) quotes a lot of examples of children carrying out subtractions, such as 305 – 97, using pencil-and-paper methods, sometimes correctly and sometimes not. Yet, regardless of whether they obtain the right answer, their comments as they perform the calculations and their explanations afterwards reveal fundamental misconceptions about the notation. The format of written calculations and the words used to explain them can themselves provide misleading cues. The same article includes an interview with a girl, Ann, who was asked to complete an addition question and began:

$$\begin{array}{r} 35\,+ \\ 17 \\ \hline 2 \\ \hline {\scriptstyle 1} \end{array}$$

Interviewer: Um... shall we go back to that little 1 that sprouted up there. You said, put down the 2 and carry 1, and I said what... Where did that 1 come from, what sort of 1 is it?

Ann: It's a carry one.

I : I see. Is it the same, you carried it with that big one there, is it the same sort of value as that big one?

A : No.

I : Oh, it's different is it?

A : Yes because it's smaller.

I : Because you drew it smaller?

A : Yes.

I : I see, what is this big 1 here worth then, 1 what?

A : 1 ten.

I : I see, and what's the little 1 worth?

A : Just 1... not 1 ten.

Given the tenuous grasp which many pupils have of the place–value notation and the misconceptions which they reveal when describing their work with numbers, it is all too easy to point to the futility of learning and performing procedures with symbols which are not understood. As a general principle, however, this needs more cautious interpretation.

The relationship between working with numbers and understanding their meaning appears in perhaps its starkest form when young children learn to count. Young children may recite numbers in order, pointing to objects as they do so. At the same time, they may not appreciate that the number of objects will be the same however they are arranged or in whatever order they are counted – the understanding of conservation of number in level 1 of this attainment target. Also they may not appreciate the ordering of the numbers, and so may not understand that five is more than two but less than seven. Sometimes, tasks which test children's awareness of these conceptual features are described as criteria of 'readiness' for number work. Yet it is hardly appropriate to argue that counting and other number skills should not be practised until these ideas are secure. Rather it seems that skills like counting and reading and writing numbers can enhance the understanding of order and conservation. Conversely, such understanding supports and reinforces the skills.

Working within a system and understanding its structure remain interrelated, whether the work involves small numbers, place value or, for that matter, negative numbers and fractions. Awareness of structural aspects of number, however, is likely to improve only if pupils can be encouraged to recognise and reflect upon these aspects. This encouragement may be provided by a real situation in which arithmetic is applied, or by pupils' own discussions and explanations of their work, or sometimes by models or diagrams which illustrate the mathematical structure. Thus, multibase (ten) arithmetic blocks might be used to demonstrate place value, and directed numbers might be represented by points and movements on a number line.

Devices of this kind are important and valuable, and provide insight in many situations. They may, however, have – or lack – features which affect their relevance to particular forms of understanding. For example, the real difficulty of some children with place value may be in appreciating the significance of the position of a digit, and multibase blocks do not highlight this positional aspect.

When a number line is used to illustrate positive and negative numbers and operations on these, the numbers themselves (such as $^{-}3$, $^{+}4$ and so on) are represented both by points on the line and by movements to the right or left. The one model incorporates two different embodiments of the numbers. Like many other forms of variety, this ambiguous model can prove beneficial, provided that the existence of the two aspects is made explicit and discussed rather than taken somewhat vaguely for granted.

The importance of reflection and discussion in using a model or illustration to enhance understanding of notation and structure needs to be recognised and emphasised. Thus, it might be thought that working with an abacus is a useful way of strengthening awareness of the positional aspects of place value. Yet, if procedures are followed on the abacus in an unthinking way, these may become nothing more than alternative rote algorithms of an apparently arbitrary nature – and difficult, elaborate algorithms at that.

NUMBER OPERATIONS

If you need to carry out an arithmetical calculation, what do you do? Obviously it depends on the calculation. If it is 6 x 7 or 6 + 7, you probably know the answer without having to think about it, and Attainment Target 3 recognises this as worthwhile learning by including addition and multiplication facts in levels 2 – 4. Of course, setting this target does not determine how it should be achieved: many people have learnt multiplication 'tables' in a systematic way which was never applied to knowledge of addition and subtraction. All this knowledge becomes familiar through usage, and acquires meaning by being used in a variety of familiar situations.

If asked to subtract 25 from 112, however, most people will use some individual method based on a mental perception of the number system. These methods are often highly idiosyncratic and rarely rely on what has been taught explicitly. Very few indeed would begin by saying' '5 from 2 I cannot take'. Again, expertise of this nature is demanded by the requirement to add or subtract mentally two two digit numbers. The prevalence of such personal methods has been recognised for quite some time. Plunkett (1979) quotes studies which suggest that by the age of 11 something like two-thirds of children already use their own processes in preference to algorithms that they have been taught. More recently, Aze (1988) has identified such abilities in somewhat younger children, and indeed amongst those who have not been taught standard written methods. These mental facilities are not necessarily a development of taught processes; rather, they seem to arise quite separately – as personal rather than official mathematical methods.

In practice, when calculations become much too difficult for informal, mental treatment they are usually handled most efficiently by means of a calculator. Many of the relevant statements of attainment refer to using a calculator where necessary, and in some cases the use of a calculator is required specifically. Planning complicated calculations and making appropriate use of the various facilities available on a calculator has become a central aspect of competence in arithmetic.

The increased emphasis on mental processes on the one hand and the use of calculators on the other represents a broadening of activity, away from the narrow concentration on pencil-and-paper arithmetic. Some people remain uneasy at this prospect, feeling that basic aspects of mathematical skill are being squeezed out. From a utilitarian point of view, however, the decline in the value of pencil-and-paper arithmetic is not in doubt. In the office, at the supermarket checkout, at the petrol pump and in many other situations, calculations are taken care of by technological devices; and skills which were once marketable have become almost obsolete. It may be that some standard pencil-and-paper algorithms can provide useful insight and experience, but this case has to be made. The reasons for teaching these methods are not self-evident.

Many skills which were familiar to the mathematically well-educated members of earlier generations have virtually disappeared from the curriculum. A standard method for finding square roots and, more recently, the use of logarithm tables to facilitate complicated arithemetical calculations are obvious examples. The position of long multiplication and long division is now dubious.

Level 5 of Attainment Target 3 requires that pupils (using whole numbers) understand and use non-calculator methods by which a three-digit number is multiplied by a two-digit number and a three-digit number is divided by a two-digit number. These demands do not appear in the earlier (NCC 1988) consultation document which declares explicitly, 'We believe that it is unnecessary to teach pencil and paper techniques for long division and long multiplication'.

Of course the wording of the attainment target does not have to imply the teaching of traditional layouts for calculations. It simply requires that pupils have some experience of performing these tightly specified calculations without using a calculator. Imaginative teaching can use this as a vehicle for strengthening awareness of place value and of the relationships between multiplication and addition, for example. Those who wish to teach the standard pencil-and-paper algorithms, on the other hand, can use this as justification for doing so. There is perhaps a danger, however, that including precisely specified tasks may give them an almost ritualistic significance which has little obvious justification.

THE CONTEXT OF NUMBER OPERATIONS

Many of the examples chosen to illustrate statements of attainment relating to number operations emphasise that pupils should not merely perform calculations but be capable of using them in appropriate contexts. Such examples include:

> Find the cost of four calculators at £2.45 each,

and

> Work out how many chocolate bars can be bought for £5 if each costs 19p, and how much change there will be.

Underlying this merging of computational skill with its application lies a convincing if perhaps oversimplified argument. We do not wish to encourage the view that arithmetic is an abstract, somewhat arbitrary game, and calculations are given meaning and purpose by the situations in which they are used.

It is important, however, to be aware that the ability to calculate and the recognition of the relevance of a particular calculation in a practical situation or a word problem are not the same. Indeed, they are quite separate aspects of achievement and they are not particularly closely correlated. There is plenty of evidence in the research literature of children who are competent in simple arithmetical calculations but are unable to recognise the need for such calculations in solving problems or to describe situations in which their use would be appropriate.

The truth of the matter is of course not that computational procedures and the choice of the correct operation have been taught in isolation from one another but that this choice has rarely been taught at all. This is unsurprising: it is much more difficult to see how to teach such recognition than to prescribe step-by-step arithmetical techniques. The increased availability of calculators brings a sharper focus to the issue. In the example quoted in Chapter 1 about the cost of 0.38 kg of cheese at £2.65 per kilogram, the real difficulty is not in multiplying 0.38 by 2.65 but in realising that a multiplication is required. The factors which make this realisation easier or more difficult have been discussed by various writers, including Bell *et al.* (1981).

Firstly, the context of the question has considerable effect on the level of difficulty: relationships are easier to recognise in familiar situations. The first APU primary mathematics survey included a notorious question about the cricketer Boycott's batting average, a setting in which many pupils were unable to identify the very easy calculation required. This is not simply a matter of prior knowledge. It might be claimed that an examination question based on, say, show jumping (see Graham 1977) needs no previous knowledge of the context provided the rules and scoring system are explained in detail. It is the ability to visualise the situation, however, and make sense of it which makes the numerical operations clear. Success in such a question is likely to depend rather more on pupils' experience of the activity than on their understanding of arithmetical operations.

Perhaps more obviously, the language and readability of the question affect its difficulty. Sometimes quite unintentionally, problems can be expressed in unnecessarily complicated words and linguistic forms which obscure the numerical relationships involved. Such questions can become more a test of reading ability than of numerical competence.

The particular form in which an operation appears can make it more or less difficult to recognise. Some children, for example, are accustomed to thinking of subtraction as 'take away' and find it more difficult to recognise it in complementary addition problems. In multiplication the Cartesian product form is especially hard; an example is given in the CSMS work:

> A shop makes sandwiches.
> You can choose from 3 sorts of bread and 6 sorts of filling.
>
> How do you work out how many different sandwiches you could choose?

It is easy, unwittingly, to introduce distractors and misleading cues into questions. Even a word like 'different' immediately suggests subtraction to some pupils – and words such as 'altogether', 'times' and 'share' have obvious though not necessarily reliable connotations.

Pupils' established misconceptions or over-simplifications are in themselves distracting. The belief, for example, that 'multiplication always makes things bigger' is fairly common; and it makes it difficult to accept that the cost of 0.38 kg of cheese at £2.65 per kilogram is obtainable by multiplication when the answer required must be less than £2.65.

Also, the size and complexity of the numbers themselves makes it more difficult to recognise the operation; it is not just a matter of the computational aspect being more difficult. Finding the cost of 2 kg of cheese at £5 per kilogram is a much more obvious multiplication.

All these considerations provide some criteria for choosing suitable situations and applications through which number operations can be illustrated, understood and used. Some care is needed with context and language, and the operations need to be experienced in various different forms.

For pupils who have difficulty with this aspect of number, various strategies may be helpful. If they are unable to visualise a situation, they can be encouraged to discuss it or to draw a picture or diagram to represent it. Sometimes it may make sense to replace awkward numbers by easier ones in order to facilitate recognition of the operation, as in the cheese example. Easier numbers make it possible to perform a quick mental calculation and to appreciate that the calculation and the answer obtained are sensible in the particular context. Knowing whether an answer is sensible is related to skills of estimation and approximation; this suggests that the development of such skills could be valuable in this area as well.

The sensible answer criterion produces an interesting twist to this discussion. It might be assumed that solving a problem set in words must always be more difficult than only carrying out the calculation involved. After all, the problem has two stages: deciding what calculation to do, and doing it. Yet there is quite a bit of evidence to contradict this assumption. Morgan (1989) provides a number of examples, including the following.

(a) $2 \div 0.04$

(b) A baker has a piece of dough weighing 2 kg.
How many rolls weighing 0.04 kg each can be made from this dough?

Children are considerably more likely to give a correct response to (b) compared with (a). Apparently the context acts as a model for the calculation, giving it some meaning and enabling sensible (and, for that matter, unreasonable) answers to be recognised.

ESTIMATION AND APPROXIMATION

Many pupils find estimation difficult. Techniques involving rounding numbers and calculating with them can prove more troublesome, and provide more scope for error, than performing the original calculations as they stand. The inclusion of Attainment Target 4 entirely concerned with estimation and approximation, in the National Curriculum requirements, highlights the need for a clearer understanding of why estimation is useful and of what strategies pupils are likely to be able to use effectively.

In daily life there are lots of situations, often involving money or time, where a rough idea of the size of the number involved is more useful than an ability to perform an exact calculation. Most people develop the ability to cope with the demands of their own situation in this respect, making sensible estimates and judgments about familiar matters.

In the article quoted earlier, Morgan shows that many pupils in secondary schools who have not been taught any conventional approximation procedures are nevertheless able to make reasonable estimates in contexts which they know and understand. They may describe their methods as 'guessing', but are often capable of offering rational explanations of what they are doing.

> 'That's nearly a pound, Miss. For a kilogram it's nearly a pound. So, Miss, I decided sixty-eight... pence for about... point sixty-eight kilograms and it's less than that 'cos it's less than a pound.'

Such reasoning, however, is less accessible without a context in which to think and talk about the amounts involved. At level 6, pupils are required to 'make use of estimation and approximation to check that the results of multiplication and division problems involving whole numbers are of the right order'. The illustrative example is:

> Estimate that $278 \div 39$ is about 7.

It would be relatively easy (and probably useful) to set this illustration in some practical situation.

The following example is more difficult to incorporate in an appropriate context, although it is admittedly at level 8 where a degree of abstractness is more acceptable:

> (Pupils should) make use of estimation and approximation to check that the results of calculations are of the right order.

The illustration is:

> Recognise that $\frac{0.25 \times 83.4}{5.7}$ is about 3 or 4.

More than most aspects of mathematical activity, procedures for estimation and approximation derive their appropriateness from the particular situation and from the purpose for which the estimates are needed. All kinds of methods and answers may be acceptable, most probably derived and expressed in intuitive terms rather than as precise rules. Pupils may need help to appreciate that such methods are legitimate and effective, especially when there is considerable emphasis on exactness and precision in other aspects of mathematics. Most of all it needs to be recognised that there are occasions when it is more sensible to estimate than calculate: without this recognition, techniques for estimation and approximation may well be seen as artificial requirements of school mathematics.

NUMERACY FOR DAILY LIFE AND WORK

Understanding number and arithmetic are given considerable priority by those who wish to provide a basis in the mathematics curriculum for children's future needs either in education or in the outside world. Within this area there are many different aspects of performance, and some decisions are needed concerning the relative value of these various aspects. All our perceptions of children's needs are distorted by our own experience, and it is worth trying to make a realistic and unprejudiced appraisal of what the real demands of the world are now and in the short-term future.

Most young people go on studying this area of mathematics after the age of 16. YTS, CPVE, BTEC and other vocational and pre-vocational schemes all have core elements, invariably involving numeracy. In a rather disturbing article, Drake and Mardell (1989) draw attention to the marginalisation of this work from the mainstream of mathematics education. Those involved in providing such courses complain in dismay at the inability of trainees to cope with supposedly elementary arithmetical tasks. For their part, young people who may well have felt unsuccessful and inadequate in school mathematics have to face more of the same. Those whose calculating skills have not been particularly good, and who certainly are not accustomed to recognising number operations in context, may be given pages of drill and practice calculations. The complexity of what is commonly regarded as commonsense mathematics is not well recognised.

The potential for intuitive and creative thinking in solving problems of a numerical nature can provide considerable personal satisfaction. It is in a utilitarian climate, however, rather than for any intrinsic value, that demands are made for greater achievement in this area. Even given this priority, the criterion of usefulness needs to be worked through. It is common to hear of employers setting tests to would-be entrants which involve items never used by any employee in the workplace and never previously met in the classroom either. If mathematics is to be more 'relevant' to life and work, then the responsibility of those designing the curriculum is to determine more honestly just what the relevant abilities are.

Chapter 3

Algebra

INTRODUCTION

According to the National Curriculum proposals, algebra develops out of the search for pattern, relationships and generalisation, and it can exist independently of the use of symbols. Nevertheless, most people would regard the use of letters as mathematical symbols as the main characteristic of secondary school algebra. The manner and context in which such symbolism is introduced and used needs careful thought. This introduction is not something which happens at a particular critical point in a child's mathematical development, and is then permanently established. From a relatively early age, it may sometimes be useful to express an abstract idea or relationship in an algebraic form, when this provides a concise way of writing down a structure which is already recognised and is difficult to express neatly in words. On the other hand, even with pupils who are older and mathematically more sophisticated, the imposition of an algebraic technique which is not seen to be necessary and not related to any familiar situation can be a source of frustration and bewilderment. Symbols, and the procedures for manipulating symbols, need to be chosen to be appropriate to the particular kind of mathematical activity, and also to be accessible and sensible to pupils. The effectiveness of teaching and learning algebra frequently depends on reconciling these two different criteria.

Although school algebra appears to involve a lot of different ideas and techniques, it is possible to identify three main kinds of activity within which these ideas and techniques are developed.

1. Generalised arithmetic: algebraic notation is used to describe arithmetical patterns, laws and relationships in a precise way.

2. Solving equations: from information given, the equations may be constructed, interpreted and solved.

3. Functions: the properties and graphs of mathematical functions are studied, leading to the development of calculus.

GENERALISED ARITHMETIC

One of the attainment target categories of the National Curriculum is both a number target and an algebra target, reflecting the view that algebra grows out of the awareness of patterns and numerical relationships. It needs to be emphasised again that this is something which can take place at any age or level of mathematical awareness. Activities which begin as arithmetical turn into algebra. It is worth looking at some examples where this happens.

Suppose we take any number and multiply it by itself. It may be helpful to begin with a largish (say three-digit) number and use a calculator, but emphasise the process by pressing the buttons which actually do multiply the number by itself – like this:

104 x 104 = 10816

105 x 103 = ?

What will happen? Will the new answer be larger or smaller (and by how much)? Or will it be the same?

105 x 103 = 10815

It is smaller – by one.

Does this always happen? The experiment can be carried out with lots of different starting numbers, and the same pattern always appears. Those who want to be clever can try fractions or negative numbers – with the same result.

To some people, this is obvious and expected; but to many, even among those with considerable mathematical experience, it comes as a surprise. Here is a general law of arithmetic, true for all numbers, of which many people will claim they were unaware. Look at it in the familiar setting of the multiplication tables:

8 x 8 = 64   6 x 6 = 36
9 x 7 = 63   7 x 5 = 35

When this law is expressed in algebraic symbols, however, it takes on a new guise:

104 x 104 = 10816 $A \times A = A^2$
105 x 103 = 10815 $(A + 1)(A - 1) = A^2 - 1$

Anyone with a background of conventional school algebra will agree that this is familiar, even if it was previously unrecognisable as an arithmetical law. It is of course possible to extend this process, by adding and subtracting 2 and then 3, and so on, recognising in the developing pattern a further generalisation.

104 x 104 = 10816 $A \times A = A^2$
105 x 103 = 10815 $(A + 1)(A - 1) = A^2 - 1$
106 x 102 = 10812 $(A + 2)(A - 2) = A^2 - 4$
107 x 101 = 10807 $(A + 3)(A - 3) = A^2 - 9$
$(A + B)(A - B) = A^2 - B^2$

Other generalisations, such as $(A + B)^2 = A^2 + 2AB + B^2$ and $(A - B)^2 = A^2 - 2AB + B^2$, can be considered in a similar light; and this consideration makes it natural to ask what these identities really are. Seen in this context, they are examples of general laws of arithmetic, which may be discovered experimentally through lots of special cases and then written in a more general form in algebraic notation. They are sometimes presented merely as specific examples of symbol manipulation – as consequences of the 'rule' which says that in multiplying together two brackets you must multiply everything in the first bracket by everything in the second. Alternatively, an area model of multiplication is sometimes used to show such expressions visually.

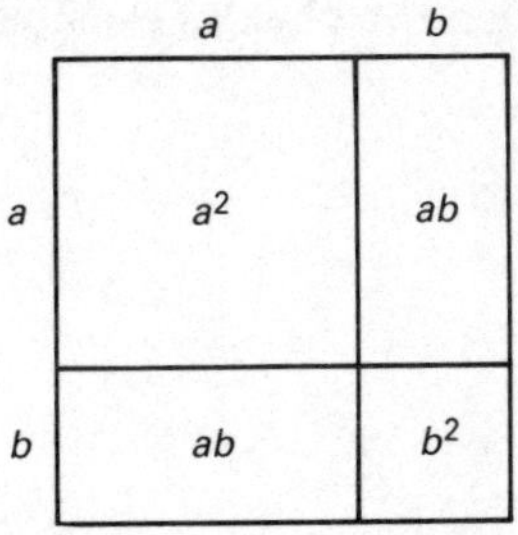

$$(a + b)^2 = a^2 + 2ab + b^2$$

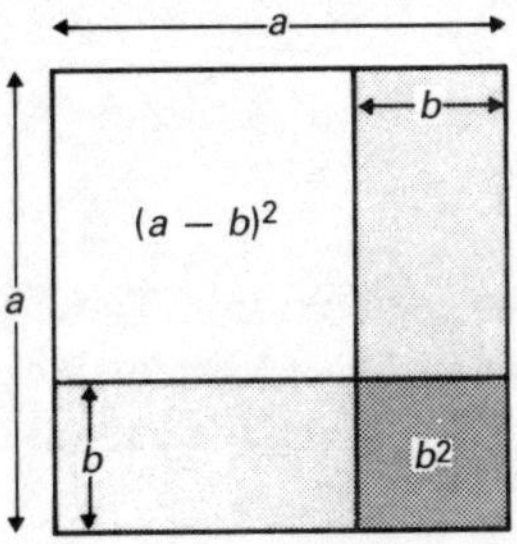

$$(a - b)^2 = a^2 - 2ab + b^2$$

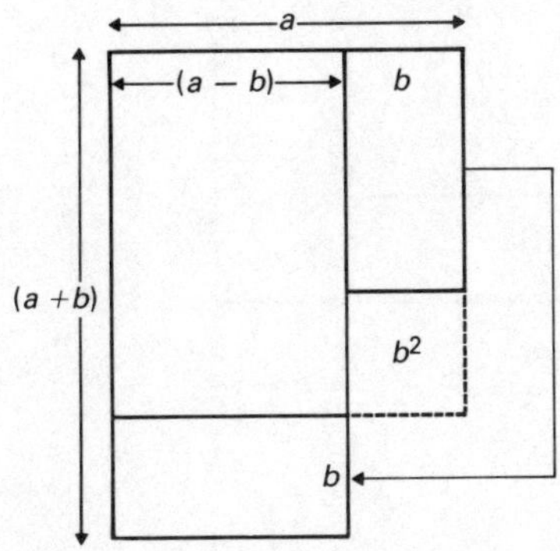

$$a^2 - b^2 = (a + b)(a - b)$$

The symbol manipulation and the area model both begin to demonstrate *why* the rule always works: they have a deductive quality which the approach based on arithmetical discovery lacks. They are alternative perspectives, and sometimes we need a variety of perspectives. Yet recognising an arithmetical law has the great advantage of providing algebraic symbolism with a purpose: the notation gives us a means of writing down a generalisation in a short, precise way which is otherwise not available. At the secondary school level this can appear a more logical reason for studying algebra than, for example, the application of equations to solving problems in supposedly real situations, which are often presented in a somewhat contrived form.

In some situations the identification of a general law or method, the manipulation of symbols, and elements of deductive argument can all be brought together in exploring and sorting out a situation. An obvious example is in the study of triangular numbers.

$$\begin{aligned} 1 &= 1 \\ 1+2 &= 3 \\ 1+2+3 &= 6 \\ 1+2+3+4 &= 10 \\ 1+2+3+4+5 &= 15 \end{aligned}$$

What about

$$1 + 2 + 3 + \ldots + 98 + 99 + 100 \quad =?$$

Or even

$$1 + 2 + 3 + \ldots + 998 + 999 + 1000 \quad =?$$

We might do all the addition, but it is surely possible to avoid this. Those who do not 'know' about summing an arithmetic progression are at least as likely as those who do to find an intuitive method – most common and most natural is to pair the first and last terms, and so on, like this:

The questions we ask ourselves are very simple:

What does each pair add up to? 101
How many pairs are there? 50

Thus $1 + 2 + 3 + \ldots + 98 + 99 + 100 = 50 \times 101 = 5050$

We could do one or two more examples, but the next question which arises is:

Will this method work for all numbers?

There could be various answers – here are two:

(a) Yes.
(b) Well, all even numbers anyway.

Answer (b) is for investigation by those who wish to tidy up all the corners; but, assuming this is a generally valid method, we might use it to develop an algebraic expression – a formula for the sum of all the numbers from 1 to *N*.

$$1 + 2 + 3 + \ldots\ldots\ldots\ldots + (N-2) + (N-1) + N = N(N+1)$$

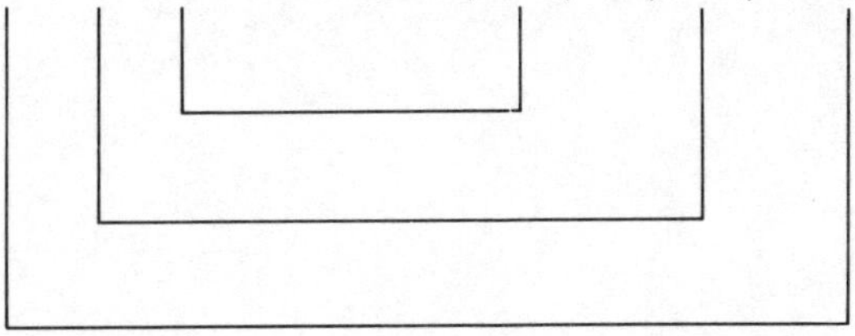

This relatively sophisticated activity is a powerful piece of generalised arithmetic. It is based on consideration of a fairly well-known pattern of numbers; but it has not been couched in terms of any real or physical problem – although it could be about stacking tins of baked beans or building blocks. Such descriptive situations have a value, particularly if they are somewhat picturesque, in that they may focus attention on the pattern and the problem; but they have an artificial feel about them. They are perhaps more correctly described as embodiments rather than applications of the mathematical activity.

Almost any familiar situation can be contrived to provide an opportunity for generalised arithmetic and the introduction of algebraic notation. For example, we might imagine a park in which all the flowerbeds are square, but of different sizes. Around each flowerbed, a path is to be made from square paving slabs; the path will be (say) two slabs wide. We might start by laying a row of slabs along one side of a square bed. When we see how many slabs long this row is, can we tell how may slabs we need altogether? What happens to the corners?

We can draw a few examples, make tables of results, discuss the pattern, describe the rule and write a formula. Activity of this nature is algebra at its most fundamental level. One of our tasks in teaching mathematics at secondary school level is to provide a range of such experiences so that pupils can learn to recognise and use patterns, relationships and sequences, and make generalisations.

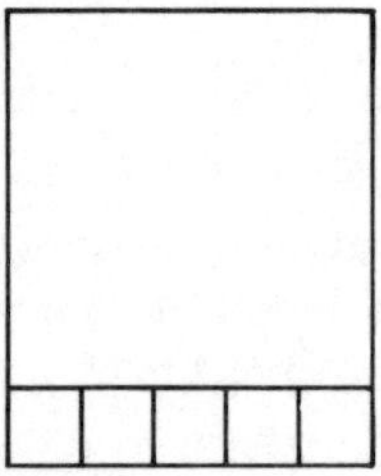

5

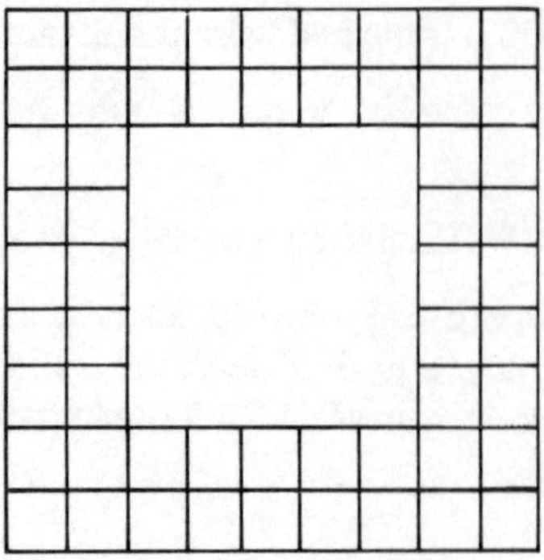

56

SOLVING EQUATIONS

In order to begin to consider the issues involved in learning about solving equations, we should perhaps start from an example which is neither easy nor an obvious choice. Let's think about

$$x^3 + x = 5$$

What does 'solving' this equation mean? It means finding a number (at the moment 'unknown') denoted by x, so that, when we work out the value of $x^3 + x$, it comes to 5. Are we certain that there is such a number? Well, when $x = 0$, $x^3 + x = 0$; and as x increases, so does $x^3 + x$: indeed it quickly becomes very large. Because $x^3 + x$ grows continuously, it certainly gets to be 5 – but only once. In mathematical language, we say that the equation $x^3 + x = 5$ has one real root.

This kind of thinking, apart from its Topsy-like metaphorical charm, is clearly trespassing on another aspect of algebra – it is a discussion of the behaviour of the function $x^3 + x$. Attempts to classify different kinds of mathematical activity have a value, and it must be important for teachers to clarify their own ideas about these matters; but this example serves to illustrate the inadequacy of pretending that there are watertight compartments.

Returning to the equation $x^3 + x = 5$, how can we find the one real root? Experienced solvers of equations will be aware that there is no chance of finding a solution as a fraction: we are talking about obtaining the answer to, say, two or three decimal places. If it were a simple linear equation, or even a quadratic such as $x^2 + x = 5$, then those who are mathematically knowledgeable might be tempted into a standard manipulative procedure – an 'analytic' solution. In this case, however, such an approach is less accessible; and, with the aid of a calculator, the most reasonable strategy is intelligent trial and error.

$$1^3 + 1 = 2$$
$$2^3 + 2 = 10$$

1 is obviously too small, and 2 too large; and in the same way the answer is quickly found to lie between 1.5 and 1.6. A reasonable approximation turns out to be 1.52.

A simple calculator is adequate for this, although the process can be carried out quickly and in a more visible way on a microcomputer with a spreadsheet facility. Throughout this activity we never lose sight of what we are trying to do in solving the equation because we are constantly reminded of it as we substitute and try out our solutions. We quickly get a feel for the kind of solution we are expecting, and in consequence we are unlikely to end up with a totally ridiculous answer. This is in contrast with step-by-step analytical methods, where a manipulative error early in the procedure may lead us to waste a lot of time and work in producing nonsense. If we want secondary school pupils to solve equations, then it is worth including activities which force them to keep thinking about what the solution of an equation means. The National Curriculum requirements recognise this by including the solution of linear and simple polynomial equations by trial and improvement methods, using a calculator.

At some stage, for some pupils at least, it becomes necessary to develop manipulative techniques. To illustrate the possibilities consider the equation

$$\frac{4x + 5}{3} = 11$$

In fact, trial and improvement is a perfectly sensible way of solving this. The analytic approach, however, can be described and set out in a number of different ways. Some texts suggest a method and layout based on identifying inverse functions: we start from the unknown x and look what happens to it in the equation – it is multiplied by 4, 5 is added, and the answer is divided by 3 – and then we work backwards. This approach has the form of a flowchart:

$$x \xrightarrow{\times 4} 4x \xrightarrow{+5} 4x + 5 \xrightarrow{\div 3} \frac{4x + 5}{3}$$

$$7 \xleftarrow{+4} 28 \xleftarrow{-5} 33 \xleftarrow{\times 3} 11$$

The solution is $x = 7$.

More common is the explanation that an equation is a 'balance', and whatever we do to one side of the equation we must do to the other:

$$\frac{4x+5}{3} = 11$$

Multiply by 3	$4x + 5$	$= 33$
Subtract 5	$4x$	$= 28$
Divide by 4	x	$= 7$

It will be noted that, although these methods differ in description and layout, all the steps in the second method are reproduced exactly, from right to left, in the flowchart above. The first method does perhaps focus more on what it means to solve the equation: we are trying to find a number x which, when we do all these things to it, produces the answer 11. But the balance idea is more widely applicable. Unlike the flowchart method, it allows us to tackle equations in which the unknown appears more than once, such as

$$\frac{x+3}{5} + 5 = \frac{2x}{3}$$

Whatever approach is taught, people who spend a lot of time handling algebraic symbolism develop their own ways of visualising manipulation. The symbols develop spatial and dynamic features: they almost acquire a life of their own. Look again at this:

$$\frac{4x+5}{3} = 11$$

Some will say that they see the 3 ready to creep out from under the fraction bar and join the 11 on the other side of the equals sign. If pressed, they may justify this by saying that they are multiplying both sides by 3, but this is not what they normally think when carrying out the manoeuvre. It is difficult to say how competent mathematicians know when and how it is correct to adopt such techniques: an over-riding control mechanism seems to develop which allows them to be used appropriately. It is not reasonable to expect pupils, who have not developed this awareness, to take on board pseudo-mathematical phrases and procedures (such as 'cancelling out' or 'cross-multiplying') and somehow know when these are valid and when they are not.

Some teachers feel a need to introduce equations when these arise in a natural context, rather than suddenly produce them. The development of a formula through the kind of generalised arithmetic described in the previous section often provides such an opportunity when the question is posed in reverse. We might for example ask how many baked bean tins there are on the bottom row of a triangular stack containing 276 tins in all, or what the length of the side of a square flowerbed is if the path all round it is made up of 130 paving slabs. Again in such examples, there is a choice to be made between a trial and improvement approach and a manipulative procedure.

Simultaneous linear equations appear at level 7 in two of the algebra targets in the National Curriculum: in one of these, the use of graphical methods is specifically required. A variety of approaches to the solution is therefore available, including trial methods, symbol manipulation and graphs. What is also needed, is a rationale and context in which such equations might be introduced.

In the Open University videotape *Secondary Mathematics: Classroom Practice* (1985), the opening sequence shows an approach to simultaneous equations. It begins with a question about buying teas and coffees: there are many similar situations, but this particular example provides us with an adequate context. Suppose in a canteen, three coffees and two teas cost £1.80. How much is coffee, and how much is tea? We can guess a number of possible answers, and even discuss which is the most likely; but we do not know. There is not enough information. There are still more activities upon which we can embark. We can make a table of the possible answers in some systematic way, we can write the information which we have as an equation, and we can draw a graph of the possible solutions, either from the table or from the equation. But what we really need is another different order; and, if we hear that one coffee and five teas cost £1.90, then we shall know which of our possible answers is the right one.

This is a relatively sensible context: it is familiar, it enables us to try a variety of approaches, and it is not too artificially contrived. Writing down a set of simultaneous equations, however, is a technique which should be used selectively, because it is often a very clumsy sledgehammer. A task which sometimes tempts experienced mathematicians into this trap is the completion of arithmagons. In these diagrams, the numbers in the middles of the sides are formed by adding those in adjacent corners.

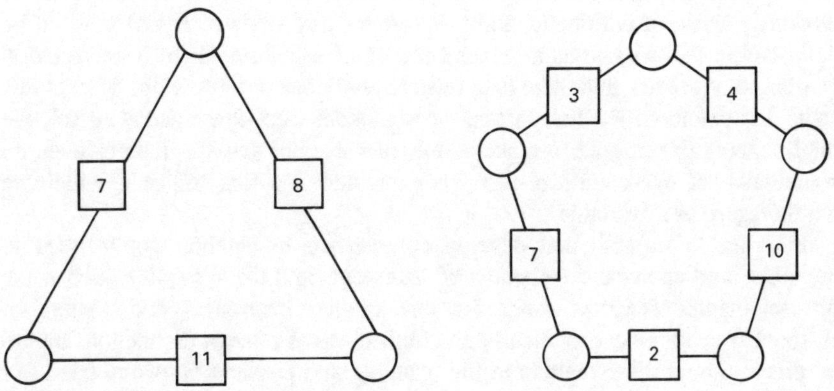

Intuitive trial and improvement methods based on the diagrams are quite effective here. Heavy-handed manipulation of sets of equations is unnecessary and unhelpful.

This example illustrates a more general consideration in introducing new algebraic techniques. It is frequently not sensible to begin with the easiest example, for which the more sophisticated procedure may well appear unnecessary. Motivation and justification for learning a new method demand the presentation of a problem which can be understood and recognised as difficult or impossible to solve without a fresh approach. A teacher who decides to talk about regarding an equation as a balance, for example, might begin with examples such as $x + 7 = 10$ and $3x = 21$. It is easy to imagine pupils looking at these and thinking 'we can do these anyway', and shutting their minds to explanations like 'take 7 from each side' and 'divide both sides by 3', which are only adding unnecessary confusion. Little do they realise that a later example will be $\frac{(3x + 11)}{5} = 10$ and they will not see the answer by inspection. To see why the new skill is needed, it is helpful to see a task which demands it.

FUNCTIONS, AND THE STATUS OF ALGEBRAIC STATEMENTS AND SYMBOLS

It has been pointed out that the identification of different kinds of activity in school algebra is not entirely clear-cut, but there are nevertheless situations in which it is valuable to be precise about the nature of statements and the status of the symbols in the statements. Consider for example:

(a) $(x - 3)^2 = x^2 - 6x + 9$

(b) $x^2 - 6x + 9 = 0$

(c) $y = x^2 - 6x + 9$

These look very alike, but they are quite different in nature. Equation (a) is obviously a law of arithmetic, and it is true for any value of x, which could be described in this context as a 'generalised number'. Formula (b) is an equation waiting to be solved, and there is in this case only one specific value of x (at this stage an 'unknown') which makes the statement true. Presented with (c), we might expect to be asked to make a table of values or draw a graph or even do some calculus. We could say that y is expressed as a function of x, which we would regard as a 'variable'.

In order to flourish and develop competence in algebra, pupils need to recognise and appreciate the status of statements and the symbols which make up statements. Teachers (and, for that matter, examiners and writers of textbooks) need to be very clearly aware themselves of such distinctions and to be precise about these matters in the planning and preparation of material. For pupils, however, success depends not so much on formal definitions of variable, equation, function and the like as on their ability to cope with these abstractions in terms of their own mental structures. We next look at some of the ways in which this does, and does not, happen.

PUPILS' INTERPRETATION OF ALGEBRA

It is some years now since Dietmar Kuchemann analysed children's understanding of algebra as part of the CSMS research project (see Hart 1981): he classified children's use of letters in algebra into six categories, which have since been much discussed. They are described as letter evaluated, letter not used (or, sometimes, ignored), letter as object, letter as specific unknown, letter as generalised number and letter as variable. Broadly speaking, the last three categories describe legitimate ways in which algebraic symbolism is used, in the three main activities of solving equations, expressing general laws of arithmetic, and studying functions and their properties.

Perhaps more than any other aspect of mathematics, however, algebra is full of mismatches. The legitimate use of symbols and the teacher's perceptions of their status may be very different from the pupils' ideas of what is happening. There are many strategies which pupils adopt which may or may not be valid, but which frequently circumvent the need for any awareness of the meaning or formal structure which lies behind the symbolism. The first three categories described above can therefore be seen not as real uses of symbols but as pupils' strategies.

EVALUATION STRATEGIES

Finding the specific numerical value of an unknown or an expression is often a perfectly valid activity. Sometimes, though, it is not; but it is not entirely surprising that some pupils fall into inappropriate evaluation.

One question in the CSMS Algebra test is :

If $e + f = 8$, $\quad e + f + g = ...$

Rather than write $8 + g$ or some similarly acceptable answer, many children provide a numerical answer. The commonest is 12, given by 26 per cent of third-year secondary school children. Another fairly common answer is 15. The perception may be that there is a pattern to be discovered, or a code to be cracked, but surely the answer must be a number.

There are a lot of situations like this in school mathematics, where it is hardly clear what kind of task is being given. Such tasks may be seen as comparable to a recent advertisement for a brand of small coloured sweets. It showed the sweets set out in an array with three gaps in it, with the caption: 'What colour are the missing sweets?' It was a good poster because it left scope for alternative thinking. Perhaps there was a pattern in the array and the gaps should complete the pattern. Perhaps all colours are in equal proportions and the gaps should make up the shortfalls. Perhaps, by buying a packet of sweets, it would be possible to find colours unrepresented on the poster which must be the missing ones. Perhaps it is impossible to tell, because there is insufficient information.

Sometimes mathematics is like this, with opportunities for creative, divergent thinking and inventing new rules and strategies. Often it is not. Pupils are expected to know the rules of play in each part of the mathematical game; and this is not always easy. Sometimes we need to spell out the rules quite explicitly.

There are situations in which, with equal validity, pupils may choose whether to evaluate a particular unknown or not. Items of this nature were first analysed by Christine Shiu, and are reported by Bell *et al.* (1983).

$$E + 17 = 36$$

$$\text{so } E + 12 =$$

Some pupils clearly evaluate E from the first equation and substitute it in the second, while others reason that the left hand side has been reduced by 5 so the right hand side must have the same treatment: the answer is 31.

There are of course similar situations in which one strategy is obviously easier than the other, but some pupils appear to have a predilection for evaluation. In this example younger pupils tended to evaluate E; and, although mathematically competent students of 16–17 were less likely to do this, many still preferred the evaluation strategy. Encouraging pupils to consider alternative and possibly more efficient strategies is one way of developing more sophisticated levels of mathematical competence.

AVOIDANCE STRATEGIES

There are two main ways of avoiding dealing with a letter in an algebraic expression: one is to keep it in but ignore it, and the other is simply to lose it altogether. Sometimes, one or other of these procedures gives the right answer. Some pupils use such strategies with considerable consistency, apparently being content with the proportion of right answers. The CSMS test provides two illustrations shown in Table 2.

Table 2

	A		B
Task	Add 4 on to $n + 5$		Add 4 on to $3n$
Correct answer, with understanding	$n + 9$	(68%)	$3n + 4$ (36%)
Keep the n but ignore it	$n + 9$		$7n$ (31%)
Lose the n altogether	9	(20%)	7
Other answer/blank	–	(12%)	–

It is worth noting that although 68 per cent of third-year pupils obtain the correct answer on task A, task B allows the identification of a substantial proportion of these who are adopting a false strategy. We need to be aware that pupils who appear to perform adequately on a limited range of tasks may be misled into relying on a strategy which is naive or inadequate or illogical, and which will quickly break down in more complicated situations.

STRATEGIES OF TRANSLATION AND ABBREVIATION

The suggestion that pupils treat letters as objects can be interpreted in two very different ways. One is that algebra consists of symbol pushing: it is a game in which letters are moved around according to strict if somewhat arbitrary rules, until all the symbols are in an acceptable formation and the problem is, or can be, solved. In one sense this is true, because the whole purpose of the machinery of algebraic manipulation is to set down problems in a format which can be treated mechanically, without the need for constant awareness of the underlying structure and detail of the problems. Most of the discussion of this chapter, however, is about providing justification, motivation, meaning and context to algebraic activity; and it is not difficult to recognise the futility of requiring pupils to manipulate symbols without any such background.

More insidious is the tendency to regard letters as representing objects, rather than, say, generalised numbers or specific unknowns. In the simultaneous equations example, the information might be represented as

$$3c + 2t = 180$$

where a cup of coffee costs c pence and tea t pence. In this situation, this reads naturally, is entirely valid and leads to a correct analysis. Pupils may translate the equation directly as

3 coffees and 2 teas cost 180 pence.

Sometimes such a perception of the letter's meaning, as a concrete object rather than something quite abstract, allows pupils to cope with statements and expressions which would otherwise be inaccessible to them. It breaks down when it is essential to distinguish between the objects themselves and the number of them. An example of the confusion then generated can be seen in expressing the relationship between a length of time (a holiday perhaps), measured in days and in weeks. Suppose d is the number of days in the holiday and w the number of weeks. What equation connects d and w? Translation suggests $w = 7d$ (a week is seven days) rather than the correct $d = 7w$. It is not an easy distinction to grasp, and there are plenty of illustrations of the confusion which arises, in the CSMS test and in other descriptions of children's work.

Sometimes concrete representations of letters are used to 'explain' basic rules for algebraic manipulation. Adding $3a + 2b$ and $4a$ is translated as 'three apples and two bananas plus four more apples' This may appear helpful initially (although it scarcely endows the activity with meaning or justification); but it is a perception which will produce a stumbling block later.

SUMMARY

In developing algebra as a part of school mathematics within the National Curriculum, there appear to be three main principles which might lead to effective teaching and learning.

The first is that the potentially most profitable basis for a study of algebra is probably not to be found in 'missing number' problems, which turn into equations to be solved. Rather, algebra is rooted in the awareness of number patterns, relationships and generalisations. The value and power of symbolic notation can be recognised most easily in the precise expression of such generalisations.

Secondly, the introduction of a new approach or technique needs to be presented in a justifying and motivating context. Often this context will be familiar and 'real'; but it need not be, providing a problem can be identified which cannot readily be solved with existing skills. What is somewhat fruitless is the development of sophisticated machinery to solve problems which can be tackled adequately without such paraphernalia.

Finally, the range of available approaches should be recognised, and sensible choices made. Trial and improvement methods are versatile, and have in the past been neglected: calculators and microcomputers make such techniques even more effective. Together with graphical and manipulative procedures, they provide a powerful range of approaches to a wide variety of problems.

Chapter 4

Measures

METRIC AND IMPERIAL UNITS

A striking feature of the National Curriculum Attainment Target 8, entitled 'measures', is the variety of units of measurement included. Established primary school practice is recognised by the requirement at level 2 to use non-standard units of length, weight and so on to compare objects: hand-spans and conkers are quoted as illustrations. At the same level, pupils are expected to know commonly used units, both metric and imperial: metres, miles, litres, pints and pounds are mentioned. Level 5 requires the use of imperial units still in daily usage, and knowledge of their rough metric equivalents.

In the early 1970s, anyone prescribing a mathematics syllabus, or producing a textbook, or, for that matter, writing for teachers of mathematics would quite probably have ignored the existence of imperial units of measurement. As decimal currency was introduced and accepted, the view was widespread – and officially encouraged – that a consistent system of metric units would be adopted in a phased but relatively speedy fashion. It has not happened, and if anything, such a planned change has become less conceivable. The inconsistency of the units used in Britain has to an extent been institutionalised. Some things are sold by the kilogram and some by the pound. Petrol may be priced in gallons or in litres, or both, but is largely sold in units of cost, like 'ten pounds worth'. Inches and centimetres are both used in describing lengths of everyday objects; but larger distances are almost invariably given in miles, and speeds in miles per hour.

In some respects, the use of a variety of units has become less important, as retail practices and buying habits have changed. Shoppers may pick up jars of coffee, pre-packed pieces of cheese, tubs of margarine or other items, making the selection by size, appearance and price and with only a cursory glance at the stated weight. In this way, as in petrol buying, the unit of quantity is by-passed and commodities are effectively sold by price. When measurements have to be made, for example in ordering carpets or curtains, it does not matter a great deal whether feet and inches or metres are quoted, provided the supplier is able to measure in the same units as the customer. This is a good illustration of the need for agreed units, and indeed the statement of attainment at level 3 includes the example

> Use an appropriate tape/ruler to compare lengths that cannot be put side by side.

In conceptual terms, the availability of different unit systems has some educational value: it emphasises that the unit of measurement is to a large extent arbitrary, that a measure is not just a number, and that quoting units is important.

THE SCIENCE REQUIREMENTS

It is interesting to make a comparison between this attainment target and the corresponding demands of the attainment targets in science. At level 2 in mathematics pupils should:

> use non-standard measures in length, area, volume, capacity, 'weight' and time to compare objects and recognise the need to use standard units',

and

> know the most commonly used units in length, capacity, 'weight' and time, and what they are used for.

In the science Attainment Target 1, level 2 demands, rather more succinctly, that pupils should:

> use non-standard and standard measures, for example, hand-spans and rulers.

There is nothing in the science requirements to prescribe the particular units to be used, as in the example provided in mathematics:

> Suggest things which are commonly measured in metres, miles, litres, pints, pounds, seconds, minutes, hours etc.

Technically, the illustrative examples are not part of the statutory orders, so that it could be argued that teachers are free at this level to adopt one particular system if they feel it appropriate. However, it is clearly intended that imperial measures should be included as they appear explicitly in the requirements at level 5.

In other respects, there is a lot of agreement between the science and mathematics requirements, although the emphasis and context may be different. At level 3, in mathematics, pupils should:

> choose and use appropriate units and instruments in a variety of situations, interpreting numbers on a range of measuring instruments.

In science, pupils will:

> quantify variables, as appropriate to the nearest labelled division of sample measuring instruments, for example, a rule.

If there is a general difference in style between the mathematics and science requirements concerning measures, it is perhaps that the statements of attainment in mathematics are more concerned with reflecting common daily usage, even where that usage is in some way muddled or imprecise. This shows up in the use of units, and also in the language used to express ideas. The word 'weight' is an unsurprising example: it is used loosely (with inverted commas) in both mathematics and science, in an everyday sense which does not distinguish between weight and mass. However, the science Attainment Target 10 on forces demands a progressive refinement of these ideas. At level 4 pupils should be able to recognise that weight is a force, but understanding the difference between mass and weight is a level 9 requirement. The word 'mass' appears incidentally in an example at level 6 in mathematics:

> Work out mean speed (distance/time), or density (mass/volume).

MONEY AND TIME

In the secondary school mathematics curriculum, the study of measurement is dominated by work on length, area and volume. Questions about money and time, when they do occur, are more likely to be regarded as applications of number than as measurement topics. Dickson *et al.* (1984), in a substantial section on measurement, point out that this emphasis is reflected in research, and the illustrative examples chosen in their review refer mostly to length and area.

Of course length, area and volume are the most perceptual, and the most intrinsic, aspects of measurement. They are attributes which are essentially more fixed than, say, monetary value, or the time taken by a task or process, or even (strictly) the weight of an object (in air, in water or at different heights above the earth). Furthermore, activities involving length and area – drawing and measuring shapes – are very much a part of school mathematics.

Handling money and understanding coinage, however, is included in one of the statements of attainment in the measures attainment target; and time appears in some of the illustrative examples. Although these topics are applications and extensions of work in number, they have particular features which merit attention.

Using coins and handling money is an activity to be found in most primary schools. Practical expertise in this area, however, is more likely to be developed outside school, particularly for older pupils, while work in school may well involve calculating and estimating costs or recording financial transactions. A written sum of money, such as '£4.25', looks like an ordinary number in decimal notation, but it may not be thought of in this way – and it may be read as 'four pounds and twenty-five pence'. On cheques, many people emphasise this view, writing £4-25p'. When amounts like this are entered on a calculator, calculations may of course produce results involving fewer or more than two decimal places. These need re-interpretation. It is clear what is meant by £4.06 or £4.60, but £4.6 is not well defined in this notation. The description 'decimal currency' requires a little modification.

The notation to represent time in hours and minutes is very commonly seen, and moves even further from a strict decimal representation. The use of digital clocks and watches and timers on video recorders and other equipment has brought a variety of situations into everyday experience which involve both expressing the time in various ways and understanding duration of time. There is plenty of scope for activity and discussion within this topic, and most children have plenty of experience to draw on. Printed material is rarely standardised or consistent. Railway timetables adopt a notation without spacing or punctuation, such as 0845, yet it is quite common to see this quoted as 8.45 a.m. No one would be fooled into thinking that *this* is a decimal point, but giving an *amount* of time in hours and minutes is a different matter. At least one local education authority, in its administration of payments to part-time teachers, uses 3.45 hours to mean 3 hours 45 minutes. Calculators do not appreciate this (unless in a special mode usually used for angles).

These considerations mean that carrying out calculations involving time brings in features and aspects of understanding which are not simply those of recognition of appropriate number operations. A clear appreciation of the relationships involved and an ability to think through a simple logical strategy are needed. Finding the average speed of a particular train from the timetable, for example, is a relatively sophisticated procedure.

LENGTH

Superficially, there does not seem to be a great deal to say about length measurement: we take it for granted that length is understood by pupils in secondary schools and that they can be expected to draw and measure straight lines using centimetres. This is not an unreasonable expectation, but is worth drawing attention to two matters of concern.

One is that a sizeable proportion of secondary pupils are not good at this work and may well need more help and practice than has been assumed in the past.

The APU review gives the percentage of 15 year olds able to make a sensible estimate of the length of a straight line (13 cm) as 68 per cent, and the percentage able to measure it accurately (12.8 cm) as 65 per cent. These are tasks which would be interpreted as only level 3 or 4 in the attainment target descriptions.

A second matter is how easily people are deceived by distracting cues or other visual features. The CSMS research (quoted by Dickson *et al.* 1984) includes the following items:

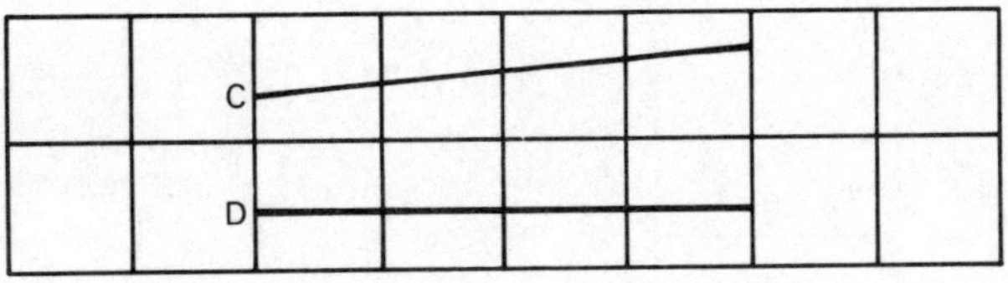

Here, more than 40 per cent of 12, 13 and 14 year olds claim that lines C and D are the same length.

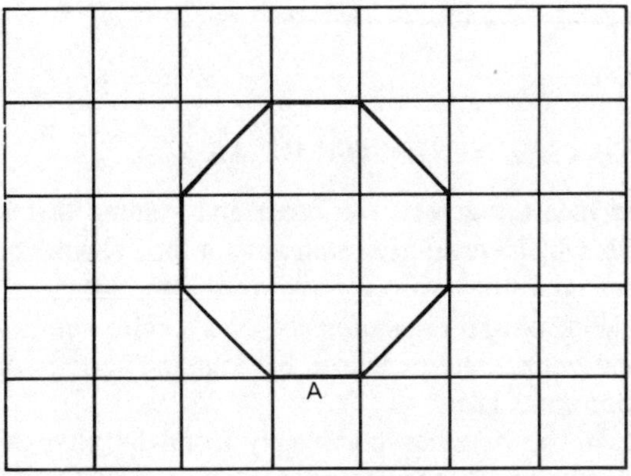

In this diagram, again more than 40 per cent of 12, 13 and 14 year olds believe that the distance all round the edge of A is 8 cm.

These difficulties in appreciating the lengths of diagonal lines on a rectangular grid, and in particular the relationship between the side of a square and its diagonal, require some attention if work on trigonometry or on Pythagoras' theorem is to have any meaning. There are a number of activities which give prominence to these relationships and provide a context and motivation for coming to terms with them. One such exercise might be the construction of cardboard models, for example of a building with a pitched roof.

Increasingly, these matters are likely to arise in computer work when this involves lines and distances on the screen. There are examples of published software (for example, the SMILE program ELEPHANT) which focus attention directly on diagonal lengths. It is in using LOGO style programs to construct geometrical shapes, however, that the need to make accurate estimates or measurements of diagonal lengths arises in the most natural way.

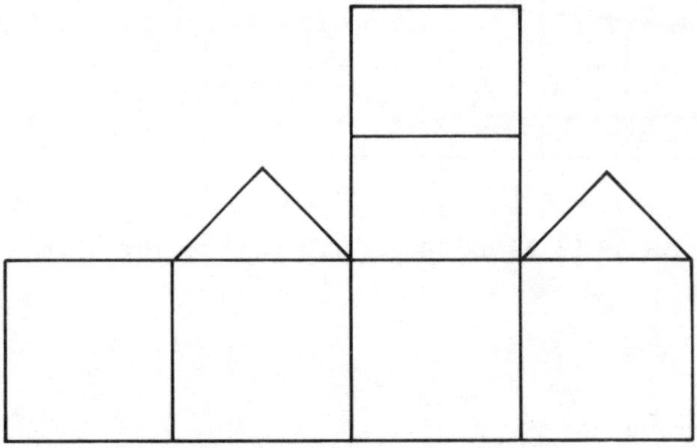

INFORMAL METHODS AND THE USE OF FORMULAE

It is characteristic of work on measuring perimeter, area and volume that it begins with naturalistic methods which encourage awareness of the meaning of these quantities, and then moves on to the use of standard formulae. String and rolling cylinders are used in work on the circumference of a circle before a formula is introduced. Area and volume are explained by counting squares or cubes, and methods of calculation come later.

Formulae and calculations can be detached completely from the physical situation. It would in theory be quite possible to carry out lots of calculations of areas and circumferences of circles with given radii, without drawing any circles or even knowing what a circle might look like. Most people would consider this to have dubious value; and yet it seems that many children do not link the formula to the earlier intuitive work, rather regarding it as an alternative, quicker or more adult method. This is illustrated in two articles by Hart (1987, 1988).

This view of two separate approaches, however, soon becomes unhelpful. A lot of tasks which are required in secondary mathematics demand some synthesis of the intuitive understanding with use of a formula. Many children make little progress in this during the secondary years, perhaps because they are not always encouraged to do so. The formula may be seen as a replacement for a naive approach: at best the two approaches may both remain available, but separately, as in Hart's (1988) study, where the children retained more than one method of finding the circumference of a circle.

Both the CSMS test paper on measurement and the CMF research used an interesting question, adapted from one used by Piaget – the 'skyscraper question':

This block is made by putting some small cubes together

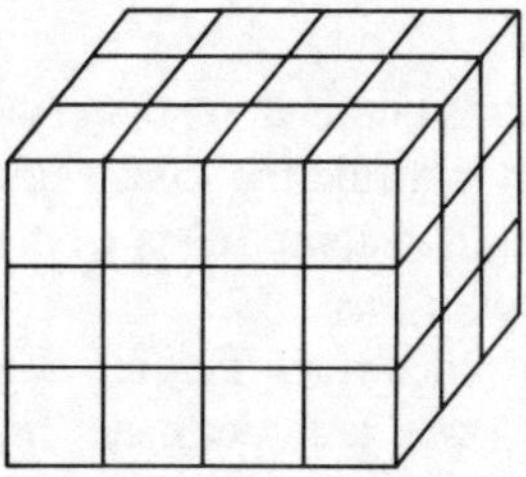

How many cubes make this block C if there are no gaps inside?

....

All the cubes from block C
are put in a pile:

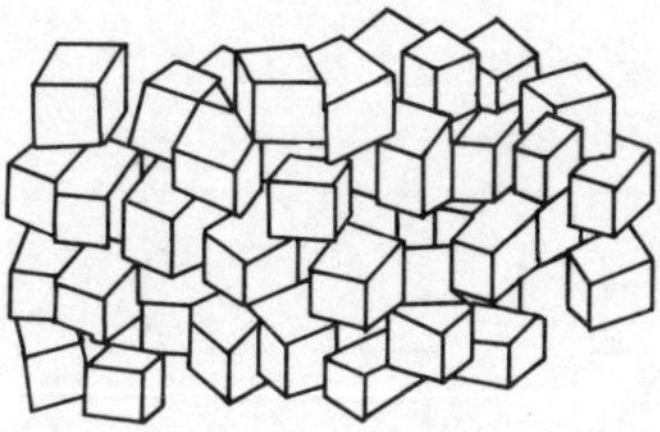

I am now going to use *all* these cubes from block C to build a skyscraper so that the bottom floor is four cubes

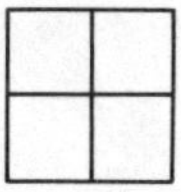

How many cubes high would this skyscraper be from the ground?

....

Here the diagram is cross-hatched to show the cubes. The question is somehow different if the block is merely labelled with the dimensions. One teacher in the CMF research retained the diagram but replaced the numbers, assuming that the children would realise that the diagram was a stylised representation of all cuboids and simply provided a frame on which to hang numbers. This is very different from seeing it as a layered stack, and much more abstract. Diagrams have a greater reality than this for many children; and a diagram drawn on the blackboard and labelled with numbers is likely to be seen as a picture of a particular block. It is important to pay attention to the appearance of such diagrams, their proportions and perspective, if they are not to mislead.

AREA AND PERIMETER

One statement of attainment requires pupils to distinguish between the formulae for perimeter, area and volume by considering dimensions. Confusion between area and perimeter is well known, and some items from the APU primary and secondary surveys reveal the extent of this.

The APU surveys have also identified the effect of using explanatory descriptions rather than the terms 'area' and 'perimeter' in items concerned with this shape:

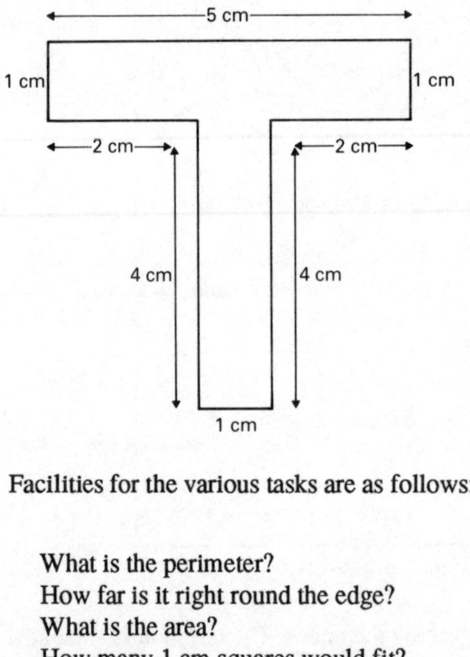

Facilities for the various tasks are as follows:

	Age 11	Age 15
What is the perimeter?	71	73
How far is it right round the edge?	76	84
What is the area?	26	58
How many 1 cm squares would fit?	56	85

The use of an explanatory phrase for area and the mention of 1 cm squares is particularly helpful. These figures show considerable development in the understanding of area from age 11 to age 15. Yet there are items in the first primary and secondary survey concerned with the area of a triangle which superficially at least are very similar and which suggest little progress:

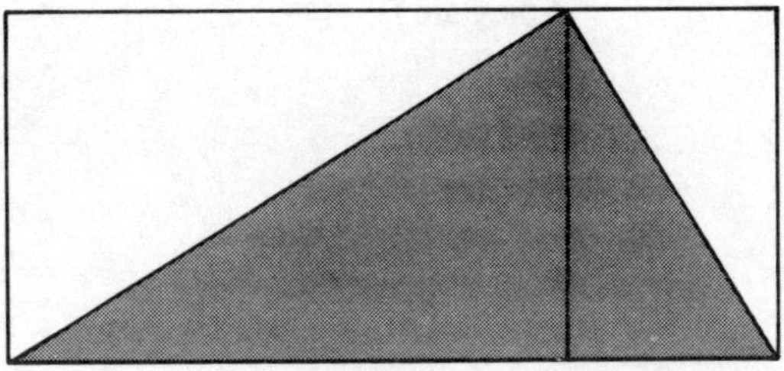

The area of this rectangle is 20 square centimetres

What is the area of the shaded triangle?

.... square centimetres

Forty-seven per cent of 11 year olds were able to complete this task successfully, while the facility for 15 year olds was still only 50 per cent.

However, the question as set to 15 year olds did not give the '... square centimetres' clue. The results from the T-shape task indicate that this may well be the critical feature, and leaving it out makes the question considerably more difficult.

These findings show that the word 'area' in particular is often not well understood; but the confusion is not simply a linguistic one – it is related to unclear usage of units and dimensions. Furthermore the confusion is not confined to pupils in schools: there are plenty of inconsistencies in the way mathematicians express problems ('a square of side 2 units and area 4 ...?'), in the way measurements of carpets and so on are described and priced (cost per metre?), and (inevitably) in the two-dimensional representation of solid objects. These difficulties merit a little more investigation and discussion: two illustrations will suffice as a starting point for this.

The first story concerns a group of teachers who met a few years ago to collect together some ideas for short assignments for GCSE coursework: most of the suggestions were for mathematical investigations at the pupils' level. One controversial problem suggested was to identify shapes which have (numerically) equal area and perimeter. Does this mean anything? Well, a square of side 4 'units' has perimeter 16 'units' and area 16 'square units'; and a circle of radius 2 cm has perimeter 4π cm and area 4π cm^2. Unfortunately, if the circle is measured in inches, the results come out quite differently. So it rather depends on the unit of measurement. Perhaps *any* closed shape can be made to have 'equal' area and perimeter if the unit of length is properly chosen? The question is not quite nonsense. But to make it precise mathematically requires much more subtle rephrasing and analysis than might be expected at this level. As it is, it simply serves to promote confusion.

As a second example, a well-known make of matches has for many years provided match problems on its boxes, among which are various demonstrations of the difficulties in dealing with dimensions. This is a classic example:

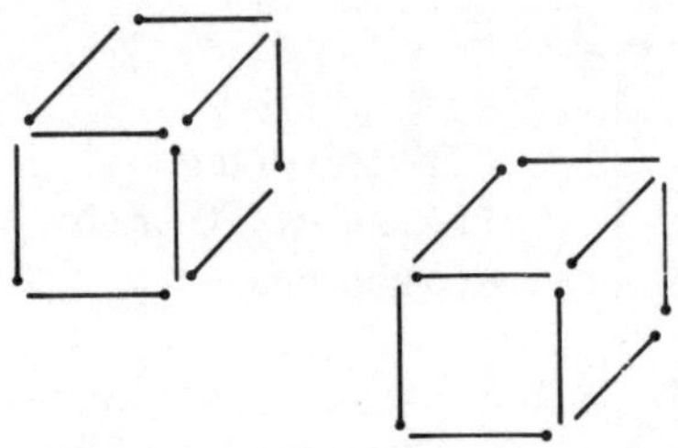

From two cubes shown combine all the matches to make one cube four times the size.

Four times – or should it be eight?

This is from the same source:

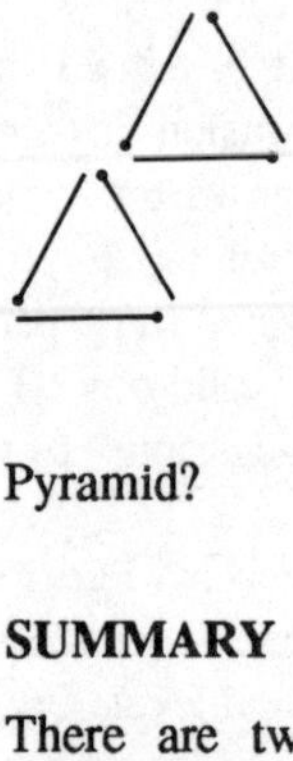

Build a third pyramid using only another two unbroken matches.

Pyramid?

SUMMARY

There are two main messages here for measurement work in secondary mathematics.

One is that there is a lot of inconsistency in the way questions of measure are expressed, in the language and units used, and in everyday applications of measurement. This confusion cannot be avoided or ignored, and there is some benefit in discussing, understanding and coming to terms with the inconsistencies.

Secondly, the development from intuitive methods to the use of formulae is not a matter of leaving one approach behind in favour of a more sophisticated one. It is not even a matter of retaining two alternative but separate approaches. There are plenty of situations where both naturalistic and more formal methods need to be brought to bear, together, in solving problems. This synthesis could be encouraged more explicitly.

Chapter 5

Shape and space

PROGRESSION AND DEVELOPMENT IN UNDERSTANDING GEOMETRY

Sometimes, school geometry can seem like a whole collection of topics and activities without any clear overall structure or direction. It may be useful to try to identify some form of progression and to express in some way just what might constitute an increase in sophistication or level of competence. The following activity and question provides a context for this:

Draw a circle and put in a diameter

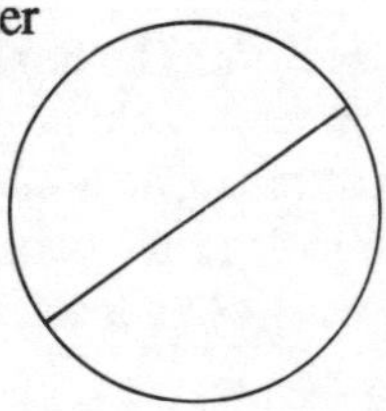

Now put in a second diameter at an angle to the first

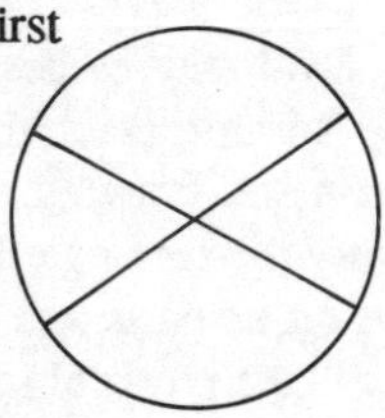

Join up the four ends of these diameters

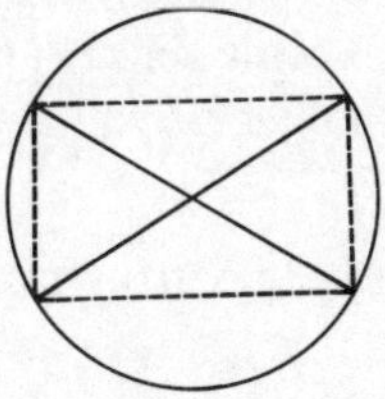

What shape is formed?

A rectangle.

How do you know it's a rectangle?

This question is a little more difficult. The intention is not so much to provide an honest, individual answer, but to determine what kinds of answer are possible, and how these might rank in level of sophistication. It is possible in this case to identify at least three levels.

If the question is given to younger children in primary school, or (equally interestingly) if we try to guess how young and unsophisticated children might respond, we obtain answers such as:

I can see it's a rectangle.
It looks like one.
I've got good eyes.
My teacher told me.

These explanations are at a *global, descriptive* level: they involve looking at the shape, recognising it as a whole, and responding accordingly.

At a different level, answers may be provided which identify the rectangle by its properties. These might be:

It has two long sides and two short sides.
It has four right angles.

This level may be described as *experimental* and *analytic*. The thinking behind these comments is that we have carried out a process akin to a scientific experiment, drawing a circle, constructing lines and taking measurements. We identify the rectangle by its properties. Rather than look at the whole figure, we focus on its parts and on relationships between them. At this level, geometry is more like a physical science.

Mathematicians, however, would want to recognise further levels of answers, which are more general and to different extents deductive. There are answers which explain how we know that the figure will always be a rectangle, however many times we carry out the process. The diagram and the construction are paradigms of a more generally defined situation, which may exhibit some variety in its appearance but has some constant properties. Thus, at a third level, explanations are given which might be called *deductive* or *logical*. One such might be:

Each of the four angles is an angle in a semi-circle, so all four must be right angles.

This particular answer depends very much on knowledge and acceptance of another geometrical law. Alternative approaches might rely on transformations or symmetry, but we produce explanations of this kind to convince ourselves (and sometimes other people) that some outcome will always occur.

Of course, geometrical work has validity at all these levels (and in mathematically more sophisticated contexts as well); but it is quite possible to see most common topics in school geometry as activities which can encourage pupils to move from a descriptive view of shape to a more analytic approach and then to making generalisations with deductive argument. A study of tessellations, for example, might begin with recognising some recurring patterns, and then drawing or experimenting with tiles or drawing to discover which shapes might tessellate:

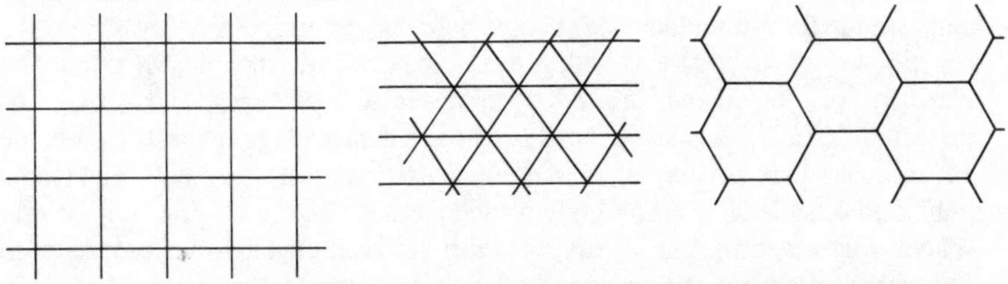

Logical argument can then arise naturally, for example in showing that the three examples given are the only possible tessellations involving a single regular polygon. At least, setting out a model of development in understanding geometry provides one view of what constitutes progression in a topic of this kind.

The idea of defining levels or stages in learning geometry has a long tradition, including Mathematical Association reports of 1923 and 1938 and a detailed scheme proposed by Van Hiele (see Van Dormolen 1977). It does not seem sensible, however, to regard these as levels of intellectual development of an individual. Rather, the degree of sophistication which pupils show in geometrical work is likely to depend on their knowledge, familiarity and confidence within a particular topic or framework. This may mean that, at any time, the appropriate style of working can be descriptive or analytic or deductive, or some transitional combination of these.

THE PLACE OF GEOMETRY IN SECONDARY SCHOOL MATHEMATICS

In the National Curriculum, there are two attainment targets concerned with shape and space. This is not a great deal: there are three number targets, the algebra categories are developed from number work and generalised arithmetic, and the work on handling data is on the whole about numerical data. Even the work on measures, although undoubtedly connected with space, can be presented as applications of number. Mathematics in the National Curriculum is nearly all about number.

On the other hand, fears that geometry might be squeezed out of the curriculum are not new and have in the past proved largely unfounded. Through the 1960s and 1970s, in newly developed schemes and syllabuses geometry moved from a standard, deductive presentation of Euclidean theorems towards a more varied, largely experimental approach to a collection of topics, commonly including symmetry, tessellations, regular solids, transformations and vector geometry. If anything, texts and schemes published during those decades increased the number of pages devoted to shape and space: some are as much as 40 per cent geometrical in content.

More recently, the efforts of a number of organisations, including the Association of Teachers of Mathematics (ATM) in particular, have been directed towards the enrichment of school mathematics by introducing varied and stimulating activities of a geometrical nature. Paper folding, the construction of geometrical solids by various means, the identification and classification of patterns, the design of boxes and packages, and a range of dissection 'puzzles' have developed from recreational fringe interests to become an accepted part of normal classroom activity in many schools and some published schemes. This is a satisfying and generally motivating development in school mathematics; but it may be difficult and indeed inappropriate to *prescribe* further innovation of a similar nature. Imaginative practical work in geometry, however, can bring a particularly attractive flavour and enthusiasm to the mathematics classroom: it may need cherishing if it is not to be stifled by the more routine demands of the National Curriculum.

The statements of attainment for shape and space refer to both two-dimensional and three-dimensional shapes, particularly at the lower levels of Attainment Target 10. Interestingly, level 6 requires the recognition and use of common two-dimensional representations of solid objects. Levels above this in both targets 10 and 11 expect work on co-ordinates, similar figures and trigonometry to be extended from two to three dimensions, apparently anticipating that two-dimensional diagrams of the appropriate solids will normally be used in this work.

Amongst teachers of very young children, the view is accepted that work with solid shapes is at least as important, and in some ways more fundamental, than plane geometry. Also, as already discussed, the construction of geometrical solids is sometimes an integral part of the mathematical work in secondary schools. Nevertheless, for many children in the middle years – in junior schools and the lower years of secondary school – there may be little work on three-dimensional geometry, even though teachers and syllabuses may pay lip-service to its importance.

It is perhaps a pity that the statements of attainment in the National Curriculum devalue the design and construction of three-dimensional solids and models by including only simple shapes, at level 4. Designing boxes or cartons, constructing models and devising techniques for building up more complicated shapes are worthwhile activities for using and applying mathematics, and they could well serve as alternative illustrations in Attainment Target 9. There is plenty of resource material for this work: the ATM materials have already been mentioned, and a lot of suitable ideas for classroom activity are also produced by Tarquin Publications.

The use of computers to generate and transform two-dimensional shapes is a requirement of Attainment Target 10. The use of LOGO in investigational work in geometry is well established, and the development of three-dimensional LOGO software allows the representation of solid objects on the screen. This creates a lot of new and interesting questions and opportunities, particularly in devising facilities to tilt, rotate or otherwise transform such representations of three-dimensional figures. These developments can provoke an awareness that some conventional representations of, for example, a cube do not correspond to a real view of a cube from any position, and new considerations are raised about the viewpoint of particular perspectives. We are accustomed to seeing solid objects on the television screen through camera shots, and it needs some care to produce graphics which appear convincingly three dimensional.

STATIC AND DYNAMIC APPROACHES

The two shape and space attainment targets in the National Curriculum are concerned with:

- recognition and use of the properties of two-dimensional and three-dimensional shapes;
- recognition of location and use of transformations in the study of space.

Like most categorisations, this is not a distinction which is easy to define clearly: it is a little reminiscent of a distinction made in the early APU surveys between 'descriptive' and 'modern' geometry. To some extent, the difference between the two attainment targets is that the first is concerned with describing and analysing static shapes and configurations regardless of where they are, and the second is about the position, movement and orientation of shapes in space. It is possible to make a distinction between static and dynamic approaches to geometry, but this is not a classification of topics: many topics can be given either emphasis. Thus, for example, reflection and rotation are the dynamic counterparts of mirror and rotational symmetry as properties of static shapes.

It is in work on angles that this distinction becomes most interesting. Early work on the meaning of angle appears in Attainment Target 11 where pupils at level 2 should 'understand the notion of angle' and 'give and understand instructions for turning through right-angles'. The examples given put this work clearly in the dynamic category. However, later work on angles in which pupils 'know and use angle properties and symmetry properties of quadrilaterals and other polygons', and then develop trigonometrical work, is in Attainment Target 10, appearing quite naturallly as an aspect of static geometry.

Once it is recognised, this dichotomy in the treatment of angles is a little disquieting. Most explanations of what is meant by an angle, angle measure or the size of an angle rely on a dynamic demonstration of rotation, or of a pair of lines 'opening out'.

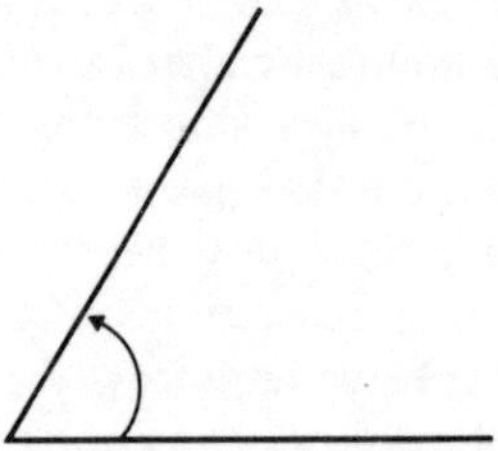

A number of computer software packages designed to teach, test or reinforce the idea of angle similarly use this approach, requiring the user to stop the rotating movement when a particular angle is reached. Yet, much work which *uses* the notion of angle is commonly presented in a static context. The sum of the angles of a triangle, for example, is usually explored, demonstrated or described in a static way. The corners may be cut off, moved around and so on, but the angles themselves are lumps which fit together to make a straight line, rather than amount of rotation. Yet it is just as possible to discuss the angle properties of polygons in terms of dynamic rotation as in a static way. Compare two approaches to finding the angles of a regular pentagon, for instance:

(a)

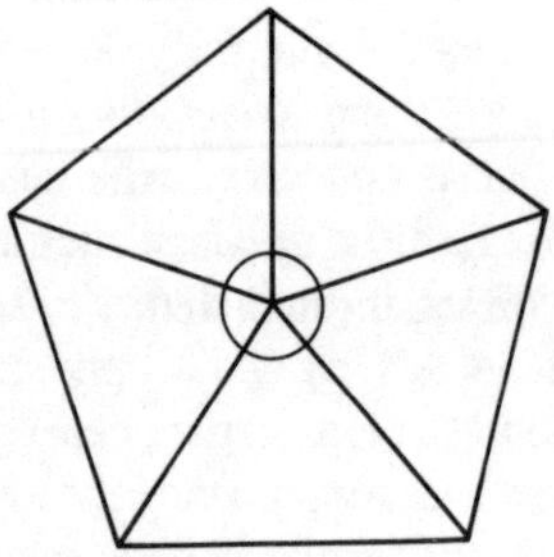

(b)

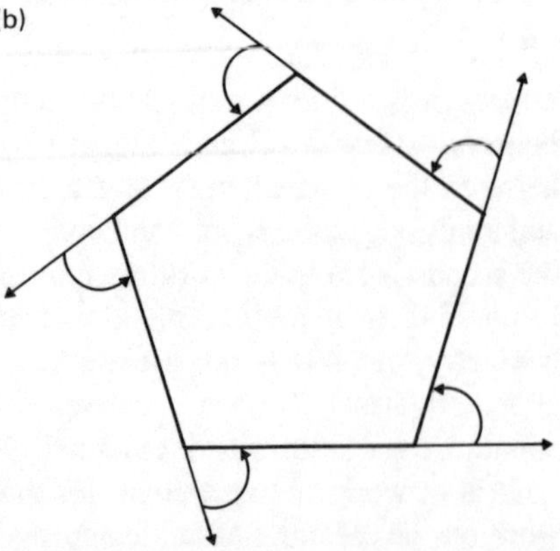

In (a) the figure is dissected into five triangles. Each angle at the centre is one-fifth of 360°, and it is relatively straightforward to find the angles of the pentagon. In (b), the pentagon is imagined as a path, the total angle turned in walking from P round to P is 360° and the internal angles can be calculated.

The two arguments are closely related, and both extend quite naturally to general demonstrations of the angle sum of an irregular polygon. They are, quite different ways of looking at the problem however. In (a) a detached observer considers and analyses the static figure; while (b) demands an envisaged intrusion into the situation and movement within it. If the main focus of attention is the angles of the (unextended, undivided) pentagon, then both methods share the disadvantage of approaching these angles indirectly, by an argument of several steps and a calculation. With just a little more effort it is possible to tackle the internal angles directly, as in the following approach to the angle sum of a triangle:

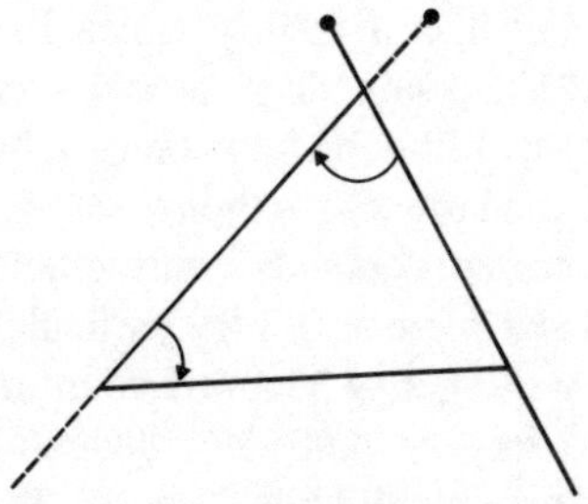

Take any triangle. Get a stick (longer than any side) and lay it along one side. Now pin it at one vertex and swing it round to another side.

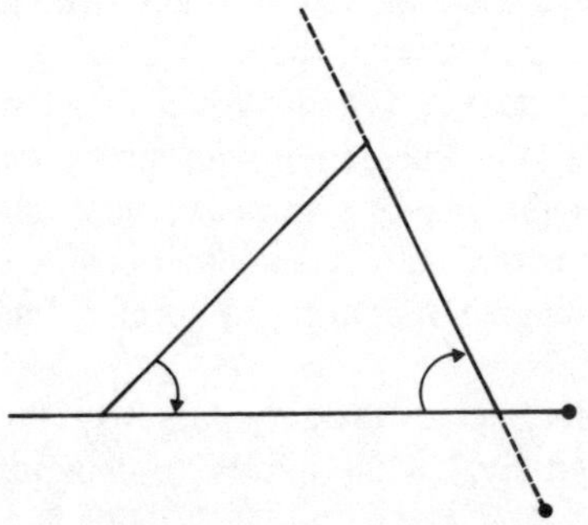

If this is repeated at each vertex in turn, the stick ends up on the side where it began – but it has turned through 180°

This demonstration is of course applicable to any triangle, and it provides a different kind of insight into what is going on here, although it may seem a little unorthodox as a 'proof'. These approaches to the study of polygons and their angle properties indicate something of the variety of possible perspectives in this topic. An experimental, discovery approach to these properties, involving the gathering of data and of experience of different shapes, can be useful – but it can sometimes give an arbitrariness to geometrical laws. They are true, it seems, almost by chance. It would be worthwhile, for some pupils at least, to *know* that the angles of a triangle add up to 180° (or make a straight line), not because they have been taught this or even because they have learned it, but because it is obvious. The interesting challenge is to make this obviousness accessible.

For quite a number of years, there have been some films available which suggest dynamic explorations of geometrical figures: titles include *Animated*

Geometry, Dance Squared and *Journey to the Centre of a Triangle*. Some use of such films is discussed in the ATM (1982) publication, *Geometric Images*; and Eagle (1989) describes how one film can provoke awareness of a general geometrical relationship. Although the earliest geometrical films are some 50 years old, however, they have not been particularly well known or very much used in schools. It might be thought that computer technology would make the production of animated sequences much easier, but it is a facility which has been little exploited. The SMILE film TAKEHALF is available as a computer program: this has some characteristics of a geometrical film, and can be used as a starting point for discussion and investigation, related to various topics.

The use of LOGO to produce designs on a screen demands considerable awareness of dynamic geometry. Even drawing a star requires a very particular insight to know what the turning angles are; and writing a LOGO procedure to produce a film sequence which is interesting to look at and also illustrates geometrical relationships and properties can be a worthwhile activity for teachers and pupils alike.

VISUALISATION AND MENTAL IMAGES

The ATM book *Geometric Images*, referred to in the previous section, is concerned mostly with visualisation, with mind pictures and with geometrical work carried out mentally rather than by drawing or making shapes. Sometimes, as already discussed, the way in which we tackle a geometrical problem demands that we envisage becoming involved in or interacting with the figure. Thus, in explaining and using the ideas of congruence or symmetry, we might think or talk about picking up shapes and putting them down in another position. In working dynamically with angles, we imagine moving and turning and walking round the figure.

In an article discussing the potential of this internal imagery, Gates (1988) describes a number of lessons which began by asking pupils to imagine something:

Imagine you are going round a race track...

Imagine a circle ...

This approach was intended to encourage pupils not to write things but to imagine things in different ways, in the hope that they might develop their own way of envisaging and manipulating structures, whether clear geometrical pictures or more abstract ideas.

There is something of a parallel here with arithmetic. It has become recognised increasingly that pupils are able to develop mental methods in arithmetic which can be used effectively. To many teachers, there does not seem any great virtue in writing everything down – especially not writing calculations in some standard format. Mental visualisation in geometrical problems is less well recognised. Those with experience of solving such problems are usually accustomed to a regime of sketching diagrams, making constructions and so on, possibly to the neglect of mental imagery.

Just as the best mental algorithm for solving an arithmetical problem may be quite different from the most appropriate pencil-and-paper procedure, so the solution of a geometrical problem may look quite different when derived mentally. It is quite surprising – and stimulating – to discover what complex geometrical designs and procedures can be envisaged without resort to drawing. One rather elaborate example will serve as an illustration.

Consider the problem of dissecting a square into acute-angled triangles. Can a square be divided up into a number of triangles, all of which have all three angles strictly less than 90°? If you have not met this problem before, try it with pencil and paper – it is not obvious.

Now, a mental solution will be described. Nothing should be drawn. If it helps, have someone else read the next section aloud to you, close your eyes and sit on your hands: all seeing and drawing movement is to be in the mind alone. Take it slowly.

Take a big square and put a very small regular octagon in the middle of it. Place the octagon so that four of its eight sides are parallel to the four sides of the square.

Mark the centre of the octagon and put in eight short spokes, like the spokes of a wheel, one to each corner of the octagon. The octagon is divided into acute-angled triangles.

Now go to one corner of the square and look at the octagon. One of its sides is directly facing you. Put out two rays, one to each end of the facing side, attaching the octagon to your corner by a long thin isosceles triangle. Then go round each of the other three corners and do the same.

Now mark the mid-point of each side of the square. Again, from each of these mid-points, put out a thin isosceles triangle to the octagon.

The problem is solved. We have an octagon divided into eight little triangles. We have eight thin isosceles triangles attaching this octagon to the corners and sides of the square. The remaining eight triangles (which take up most of the space) are almost (but not quite) right-angled: they must be acute-angled.

As soon as you are convinced that this is a solution, open your eyes and forget it. It is not of course the only solution, and there are dissections requiring fewer triangles (see Bolt 1985); but it shows that a complicated geometrical figure can be described and assimilated mentally, without recourse to drawing. Moreover, that process is quite exciting. Internal visualisation is a more powerful resource than is commonly realised.

Chapter 6

Handling data

STATISTICS IN THE SECONDARY CURRICULUM

The introduction of statistical ideas in school mathematics has developed historically from two ends. The collection and representation of information is an established part of work in primary schools, where block graphs, pictograms and mapping diagrams are commonly on display. In sixth forms, since the 1960s, A-level syllabuses in Pure Mathematics with Statistics have grown in popularity compared with courses including mechanics. For the 11–16 age range, however, work in statistics has grown much more slowly, so that the inclusion of three attainment targets in this area in the National Curriculum gives it a prominence which it has not previously enjoyed in the great majority of secondary schools.

The relative neglect of statistics by those interested in mathematical education is reflected by the paucity of articles concerned with this topic in *Mathematics Teaching* and *Mathematics in School* over the years. There is a specialist journal *Teaching Statistics*, but, at least until recently, most of its coverage has been more relevant to sixth-form and higher education than to mainstream secondary school work.

The umbrella heading 'handling data' in these attainment targets covers a slightly broader range of activities than might traditionally be described as statistics. For example, work with computer databases, involving the storage and access of information, is included. The background to this development is discussed in an article edited by Green (1988) which provides some clues about the direction which statistical education might take, and begins to explore the relationship between statistical awareness and the so-called 'explosion' in information provided by new technology.

Conscious of the need to provide materials which enable pupils to recognise and use the tools and techniques of information technology, the Microelectronics Education Support Unit (MESU) produced in 1989 an 'Information Handling Pack', including computer software and support material. The pack includes a number of classroom reports: these are from primary and middle schools, but the facilities which the pack provides are a useful resource for all kinds of work in both primary and secondary schools. Sometimes this is a matter of understanding the facility itself – recognising how data may be entered, reorganised and retrieved in a required form. On other occasions, pupils may be able to use devices which would otherwise prove difficult or tedious. For example, it is a difficult and sophisticated operation for many pupils to draw an accurate pie chart; but the ability to do this on the computer – and, importantly, to print it out – allows them to talk about, interpret and understand such a chart without needing the technical skill to construct one. This experience may itself provide the insight and the motivation for pupils to develop the awareness of relationships and subsequently the skills to draw a pie chart, if this is considered important.

One of the early comments made by teachers who have used software of this kind is that the information collected is a means to an end and not an end in itself. This means that care needs to be given to questions such as the following:

- Why am I collecting it?
- What do I hope to find out from it?
- How can I ensure the accuracy of what I collect?

These considerations lead to a fundamental issue in statistical education: there are two different ways of looking at the subject. One is that there is a large collection of statistical ideas and techniques which we want to teach and learn, and we must find suitable examples and activities to illustrate these. The alternative view is that there are a lot of questions and situations which we want to explore and understand, and access to a range of statistical devices will help with this. The dilemma is that setting out statements of attainment relating to specific knowledge and processes inevitably suggests the first view, while many teachers would want to encourage the second.

The idea that statistics is taught and learned most effectively in the context of projects which explore issues rather than as a set of skills and processes which have familiar illustration is common in published suggestions. Ernest (1986), for example, describes some work in school on statistics and the media. The Schools Council Project on Statistical Education (1975–80) produced a large number of booklets of statistical work, with titles such as *Smoking and Health* and *Car Careers;* all begin with a situation or an issue and develop relevant statistical material. In a letter from Hungary, Szendrei (1989) indicates a similar approach, claiming that 'the students find the concepts of statistics natural, because they need them in order to solve the problem'.

The challenge is to sythesise the different objectives to produce a range of realistic activities and questions which will allow the development of all the statistical work considered appropriate. If it then turns out that there is no familiar or sensible context in which the need for a particular idea or technique is recognisable, this is a good reason for questioning its place in the curriculum.

STATISTICAL CALCULATIONS

The statements of attainment relating to the collection, recording and processing of data include the requirement that pupils should

> understand, calculate and use the mean and range of a set of data,

and later

> find the mean, median, mode and range of a frequency distribution for a given set of data and interpret the results.

The illustrative examples show likely contexts, and confirm that these procedures are intended to be developed within familiar situations. Statistical awareness in daily life, however, rarely involves carrying out calculations – rather it involves being presented with the results of other people's calculations and having to make sense of them. Frequent publicity is given to the retail price index, the rate of inflation, the level of unemployment, the 'average' rise in wages, the *Financial Times* share index and a variety of other numbers; and information is often presented in graphical form. Experience of using a computer facility has indicated that pupils are able to discuss, interpret and understand a pie chart, for example, without necessarily possessing the skill to construct one accurately. Similarly, being able to calculate averages may not relate closely to the ability to understand and discuss their implications.

Goodchild (1988) describes this facility as a *reverse process* which cannot be taken for granted: opportunities for considering what a stated average is telling us should form at least as important a part of statistics teaching schemes as the methods of calculation. He draws attention to earlier studies which demonstrate that for many students dealing with the mean is a computational process rather than a helpful idea. Learning to calculate a mean is not the same as appreciating its purpose in giving some easily digested information about the whole population.

Goodchild used matchboxes on which was printed 'Average contents 35 matches' as the basis of interviews with pupils in which he tried to relate the discussion of average to their everyday experience. The implication of this work, and of much of the discussion in this field, is that it is insufficient to proceed purely in the direction of beginning with a collection of data and carrying out calculations. Pupils also need the experience of making interpretations about unknown data sets on the basis of measures of data given to them.

GRAPHICAL REPRESENTATION

Attainment Target 13 is all about the representation of data in pictorial, tabular and graphical form. It is full of statements requiring pupils to 'construct, read and interpret' various categories of diagram. The levels are a natural attempt to order the various forms of representation in increasing sophistication. One of the problems in defining these levels is that construction and interpretation may present a considerable difference in difficulty: pie charts, for example, which appear at level 5, may well be rather easier to understand and interpret than to construct. The APU reports confirm that reading a graph is often easier than drawing one.

Some of the issues involved in developing a progression of work on graphical representation are explored in a recent series of articles by Gallimore (1989). Until the development of the National Curriculum, the approach has been very haphazard, with some topics repeated over and over again from early primary school right through to secondary school providing no apparent progression. Even where detailed records and progress charts have been kept and passed from one year to the next through primary school and then on to secondary school, experience of graph work has rarely been included. At least, the specifications of the National Curriculum may clarify this.

Gallimore's view, however, is that a major problem in ensuring a clear understanding of graphs is their universal nature. Graphical representation of one kind or another permeates almost every subject in the curriculum, and work involving graphs has become increasingly popular in stimulus or comprehension questions in examinations in a variety of disciplines. Teachers specialising in subjects other than mathematics may well assume wrongly that their pupils possess very sophisticated graph skills, and difficulties inevitably arise from this assumption. The recognition that this topic in particular and to some extent all statistical work can be identified and used in many school subjects reinforces the recommendation in the Cockcroft Report that efforts should be made to ensure that there is co-operation in this area, and that, in secondary schools, one member of staff might be nominated as statistics co-ordinator.

PROBABILITY

The final attainment target demands that pupils should understand, estimate and calculate probabilities. As well as these formal, numerical aspects of probability, it includes the recognition that there is a degree of uncertainty about the outcome of some events and other events are certain or impossible, and also ideas of 'fair' and 'unfair'. Some further indication of the kind of work expected is provided by the applications suggested in Attainment Target 9. Pupils should 'make and list predictions', and this is illustrated by the following.

> Experiment with a collection of dice with different numbers of coloured faces; predict the outcomes of rolling each die 50 times and test the predictions.

The words 'predict' and 'prediction' are used very freely in the National Curriculum for mathematics, in a variety of contexts and with different shades of meaning. Fielker (1989) discusses these nuances in some detail – it is clear, for example, that 'predict' in Attainment Target 1 is not the same as a prediction based on probability, or is it?

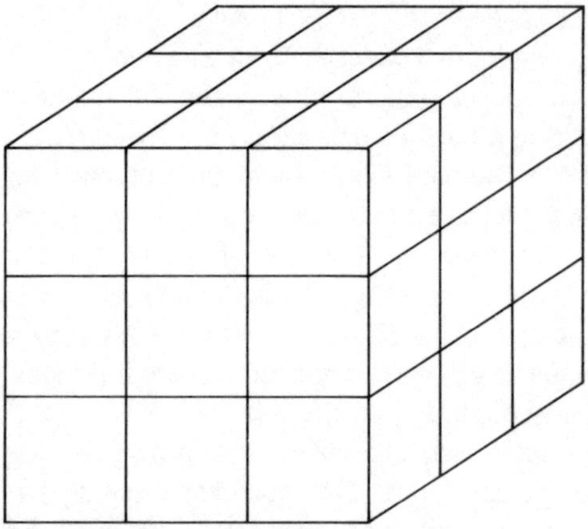

Predict the number of cubes needed to construct this figure and test the prediction.

In probability, at least, prediction is presumably to do with not being sure, but believing something is likely – or, in some cases, believing that an estimate is reasonable. In the cubes example, if the prediction turns out to be inexact, we revise our thinking about the situation. In the dice question, we do not expect to find precise agreement – but extreme mismatch would force us to reconsider the theory or the calculation.

In this attainment target three different perceptions of probability are intertwined.

The first perception involves the construction of a mathematical model to describe a situation in which chance plays a part. This model may involve enumeration of possible outcomes, consideration of independence of events, and use of addition and multiplication rules. Care may be taken over these theoretical considerations and over the calculations, but in the end the model may or may not prove a good predictor of the relative frequency of actual events. A theoretical approach of this kind is usually illustrated by examples about coins, dice or drawing coloured balls from bags.

A second view is that probabilities may be found empirically. Pupils should 'understand and use relative frequency as an estimate of probability', and this is illustrated by the example:

> Estimate by experimentation the probability of a drawing pin landing on its base.

These two notions of probability are differentiated explicitly. In one of the statements of attainment, pupils should

> distinguish between estimates of probability based on statistical evidence and those based on the assumptions of symmetry.

'Equal likelihood' might be a better expression than 'symmetry' here, and indeed this is the phrase used when a third idea of probability is introduced. Pupils should

> when assigning probabilities appreciate that relative frequency and equally likely considerations may not be appropriate and 'subjective' estimates of probability have to be made.

The example corresponding to this statement is

> Recognise that the statement 'There is a 0.1 probability that a cure for cancer will be found in the next two years' cannot be based on evidence.

Nothing is entirely subjective: this example confuses the issue a little because the difficulty in determining the probability is exacerbated by the inadequate definition of the event. Cancer covers a range of conditions and the meaning of a 'cure' in this context is debatable. More clearly defined events, of which any estimate of probability must be to a large extent subjective, include the following.

- Nottingham Forest will win the F.A. Cup next year.
- The Conservatives will win the next General Election.
- The next President of the United States will be a woman.

The admission of uncertainty which prediction of events demands is often difficult for pupils to express. When asked, for example, 'Will the telephone ring in the next hour?', young children in particular are likely to answer yes or no and wait to see if their guess is right. The APU surveys include items such as

> If I roll the die 18 times, how many times will each number come up?

As a test item, the question could be improved; but, almost inevitably, pupils at both age 11 and age 15 give a definite answer to the question rather than explain the kind of uncertainty involved.

The application of addition and multiplication laws to determine the probabilities of combined events in a theoretical model appears at level 7 and above. Levels 8 – 10 are concerned entirely with work of this kind. Success in this area is likely to remain very much a minority accomplishment: the APU reports quote facilities less than 10 per cent for 15-year-old pupils on items of this nature.

Chapter 7

The broader curriculum context

INTRODUCTION – DELIBERATE AND UNINTENTIONAL CURRICULA

The main concern of this book is the teaching and learning of mathematics in the 11–16 age range. The objectives to which this teaching and learning is to be directed are specified in the National Curriculum requirements. Even in lessons labelled 'mathematics', however, pupils will learn plenty of things which are not set out in the attainment targets, some worthwhile but others counter-productive. Prescribing an official curriculum does not ensure control of this learning – rather the reverse. Research on the so-called hidden curriculum suggests that an unintentional curriculum is likely to grow up alongside the official one.

While the National Curriculum sets out the content of school subjects in considerable detail, it is in other respects remarkably silent – and in some cases quite deliberately so. There is little concern for gender or multicultural issues, and consideration of emotional and attitudinal aspects of learning mathematics has been largely squeezed out. Children have always learned about gender and race in school and have always developed affective responses towards school subjects, and recent changes in secondary schools have tended to bring these issues into official school policy in the hope of exercising a measure of control over them. At the same time, there has been some simplistic reaction against this trend. These are social issues, it may be claimed, and schools are for education, not social engineering. Like it or not, however, the development of social attitudes and relationships is a large part of children's school experience. This development colours their motivation and progress, and has the potential to be a major influence in adult life. Ignoring these matters, or failing to regard them as the concern of teachers and curriculum planners, allows a lot of the culture of school life to grow in an erratic, clandestine and potentially perverse way.

The importance of teachers' awareness of issues of gender, culture and affective response is recognised by later chapters concerned with these matters. The present chapter, however, deals with the broader deliberate curriculum within which secondary mathematics education is nested. By the age of 11, children already have a lot of experience of school mathematics; during the secondary years, they meet mathematical demands in a range of other subject areas; and some go on to more mathematics after the age of 16.

MATHEMATICS IN PRIMARY SCHOOLS

Some of the saddest stories of children's mathematical development centre on the transition from primary to secondary school. Children may be told that this is a fresh start – with the underlying message that what has gone before is of no importance. Primary school teachers visiting their former pupils in their first year in secondary school have been known to be outraged at the apparently undemanding and uninspiring work in mathematics. Whether or not these stories are typical – and even if they are apocryphal – they strike a chord in their unease about perceived lack of recognition by secondary teachers of the value or even the nature of primary school mathematics. It has been possible for some large schools to point to the great variety of schemes, syllabuses and approaches used by their feeder primary schools as an obstacle to this recognition.

At least, the National Curriculum has the potential to bridge the transfer between primary and secondary school. The programmes of study define a common core of background experience, the attainment targets provide continuity, and the arrangements for record-keeping and reporting should ensure that adequate information about pupils' levels of achievement is available to their new school. Knowledge of the content and nature of mathematics in feeder primary schools has always been valuable to secondary teachers: the National Curriculum ought to make this more difficult to ignore.

A useful survey of the state of primary mathematics is provided by the HMI (1989) publication, *Aspects of Primary Education: the Teaching and Learning of Mathematics*. This booklet is based on inspections of and visits to primary schools during the 1980s: it gives an overview of the situation and identifies a lot of good practice as well as some deficiencies.

Some good primary practice is thematic and integrated, so that it may be possible to identify mathematical learning but at the same time difficult to quantify this as a proportion of children's activity. On the other hand, most primary schools devote quite a lot of time specifically to mathematics; and overall the subject represents on average about 23 per cent of teaching time – equivalent to more than one full day per week. Some classes of junior-aged (7–11 years) pupils have been identified as spending a disproportionately large amount of time on mathematics: in many cases, this is associated with a narrow emphasis, usually on arithmetical skills.

On the whole, the demands of the lower levels of the various attainment targets are based on successful practice already identified in many primary schools. HMI assessments during the 1980s have regarded the bulk of primary school work in mathematics as satisfactory, although there is considerable unevenness across the various elements of the subject.

Number work, particularly arithmetical computation, has always been given a lot of attention. In the vast majority of primary schools, most children develop adequate performance skills in arithmetical calculations. Even so, in many cases, pupils may be unable to apply these reliably in practical situations or to have sufficient understanding to estimate whether an answer is reasonable. Almost all schools extend this work to fractions, decimals and percentages; and again pupils develop at least adequate ability in calculations involving decimals in most schools. Understanding of ideas related to fractions, however, is often relatively limited: arithmetic involving fractions is quite commonly taught, although its appropriateness may be questioned.

Work on number patterns has an established place in primary school mathematics. Children create series by repeated addition or subtraction, investigate patterns in the multiplication tables on a 10 x 10 grid, and in some cases use calculators to generate sequences. These activities reinforce knowledge of multiplication tables, and, as already suggested, can provide a good starting point for introducing algebra.

Weight, length, area and volume are commonly introduced in primary schools, mainly through practical activities and often using non-standard units in the first instance. Work on time is also a normal part of the primary mathematics curriculum, although many schools continue to emphasise the traditional clock face and give little attention to digital display. In spite of this, the majority of 11 year olds are able to handle both formats competently.

In shape and space, the development of primary school work has been more patchy, and children's experience and consequent understanding is variable. In Chapter 5, the somewhat unstructured nature of geometrical work was mentioned; and, until the development of the National Curriculum, an adequate rationale for this work, leading to reasonable performance, existed in probably no more than half of all primary schools. On the other hand, a minority of schools have developed a particular strength in this area, with good work on both two- and three-dimensional shapes, exploration of angles, co-ordinates, symmetry and tessellations, and in some cases the use of LOGO to extend the investigation of geometric patterns.

Nearly all primary schools include work on data handling, in particular collecting information and representing statistics in pictorial or diagrammatic form. The results of such activity are often displayed in drawings and models.

The normal teaching arrangement in primary education is for one teacher to be responsible for all or most of the work of each class of children. This structure allows flexibility in the daily programme, and enables project and topic-based activity to be planned to cross a range of subject areas. Although most schools have established some cross-curricular links, however, mathematics is most often presented as a discrete study. Only about one school in six is successful in integrating mathematics with other areas of the curriculum in a sustained way.

The majority of junior schools make extensive use of a published scheme of textbooks or workcards. The small minority of schools which do not use such a scheme contains extremes of performance. Some are very successful in mathematics, where enthusiastic teachers have developed their own materials; while others lack guidelines and common policies so that the work has no coherence.

Most primary school teachers tend to group children within their classes by ability for work in mathematics. This may prove convenient for setting work and using materials; but there is no evidence that any particular way of organising teaching groups has a direct effect on the pupils' levels of achievement.

Only about 4 per cent of primary school teachers have a main qualification in mathematics. However, in most schools a designated teacher has responsibility for the subject – these are often teachers who have developed this interest while in post or by attending in-service courses. These mathematics co-ordinators may act as consultants to other teachers, but are rarely involved in specialist teaching of classes other than their own. It is commonly believed that they could be more effective if given time to work alongside other members of staff, but few do this: staffing arrangements in most primary schools make such a practice difficult to organise.

MATHEMATICS ACROSS THE CURRICULUM

The non-statutory guidelines to mathematics in the National Curriculum provide a rationale for cross-curricular work. As these guidelines indicate, experiences in life do not come in separate packages with subject labels. The structure of primary schools allows scope for exploitation of mathematical features and processes in a variety of themes and topics, although even at this level the opportunities are underdeveloped. In secondary schools, a thematic approach is much rarer; and, even in those schools where integrated studies or interdisciplinary enquiry has formed the basis of the time-table, mathematics has often been removed from this structure and discrete lessons allocated to the subject.

To be realistic, the compartmentalisation of subjects in the National Curriculum and the departmental structure of secondary schools taken together are not going to produce extensive cross-curricular projects or integrated approaches. The best hope is that activities in each subject area can recognise and draw upon experiences in other subjects. The non-statutory guidelines suggest two issues for secondary schools:

- the identification of the uses made of mathematics across the different subject departments;
- systems for co-ordinating approaches to the teaching, learning and using of mathematics across different subject departments.

Taken alone, these statements appear to suggest a one-way traffic. Mathematics is learned and used in mathematics lessons, but also appears in other subjects.

Yet, it is at least as important that the work in mathematics lessons draws upon other subject areas, and involves incidental learning related to these subjects – otherwise the view is likely to be promoted that mathematics lessons are not really about anything at all.

Perhaps the way forward is to try to develop themes, topics, activities or whatever in a well-defined package of lessons which might form a scheme of work in mathematics or another subject – or in both, although this will most probably depend on individual co-operation between members of staff responsible for classes. Differential setting of pupils between subjects makes this difficult too. In outlining interdisciplinary activity of this nature, it might seem most obvious to link mathematics with technology or physical science. Those who have explored the possibilities, however, have tended to avoid the obvious.

Probably the most extensive investigation of the links between another subject and mathematics is that provided over the years by Selkirk (1982) in a series of articles and a book *Pattern and Place*, describing the relationship between mathematics and geography. A lot of the activities suggested could form a basis for development of the National Curriculum requirements in mathematics – there is interesting work on measures, co-ordinates, geometry and, of course, statistics.

Another, more recent, substantial collection of material can be found in the extremely attractive series of articles in *Mathematics Teaching* by Grevsmuhl (1988–9) linking mathematics with art. Themes which may be explored through pictures include number patterns, transformation geometry and even chance and probability. One article is concerned particularly with computer graphics, and it may be in this area of development that the integration of mathematics and art work is most likely to grow.

Mathematical ideas and activities in the context of textiles and needlework are identified by Watson (1988) and Harris (1988). As Harris explains, the whole of textile work, construction, decoration and use is full of mathematical thinking. There is scope for work on geometry, measurement and ratio, and a whole range of strategic and optimisation problems to be solved.

Tytherleigh and Watson (1987) discuss the relationship between mathematics and dance, and offer some realistic classroom suggestions. They suggest that the affinities between music and mathematics are relatively obvious and reasonably well documented; but, at least at the level of secondary education, there is little evidence of this. It is a common but largely unsubstantiated belief that aptitude in mathematics and music are linked; and certainly mathematics and music lessons in secondary schools have little common ground. There is scope for development in this area: some starting points are suggested by Land (1975). The mathematical topics developed include number patterns, indices, graphical representation and ratio.

On the whole, the demands which the production of an interdisciplinary programme of work makes on teachers are somewhat greater than the more familiar demands of specialist subject teaching. There are not likely to be published schemes, textbooks or worksheets available which can be used directly by classes; and, given the staffing patterns of secondary schools, at least one of the subject disciplines is likely to be unfamiliar. Yet the pay-off for the teachers involved is likely to be positive in terms of developing new and interesting work and being able to present pupils with a less fragmented experience.

In certain respects, the National Curriculum encourages cross-curricular work. The ideas and techniques specified by the attainment targets for handling data could arise and be useful in any subject area. The non-statutory guidelines advocate cross-curricular approaches. On the other hand, the tight categorisation of subjects and specification of attainment targets within subjects suggest a narrower focus. Perhaps the combined effect of these conflicting messages will be broadly neutral, and the extent of worthwhile cross-curricular work in secondary mathematics will, as before, be limited to a relatively small number of programmes, developed by enthusiasts.

POST-16 MATHEMATICS EDUCATION

As indicated in Chapter 2, most young people continue to study mathematics after the age of 16. Vocational courses and employment training schemes include an element of numeracy. Among those who continue in academic education, however, there is a very clear divide between those who study mathematics and those who do not. Unlike many other countries, there are no core elements in courses at sixth-form level in Britain.

For quite a number of years, sixth-form courses have seen less upheaval than any other sector of education. The introduction of GCSE quickly followed by the National Curriculum has created a period of rapid change in the main years of secondary schooling; and most higher education courses, particularly those in polytechnics and colleges, have had several years of turmoil. The general stability of sixth-form courses has been reflected by the lack of any radical review of, in particular, the structure of A-level mathematics. This means that the traditional A-level syllabus is no longer a natural follow-up to most GCSE courses, and is arguably not very appropriate as a starting-point for many courses in higher education. In spite of a certain political reluctance, some change now appears inevitable.

The changes in the parameters which surround sixth-form mathematics happened quickly. At the time of the Cockcroft Report (1982), A-level appeared less like an island; but, even in that report, there are indicators for development which have since become more urgent.

One consideration is the style of A-level courses, which are on the whole very different in terms of teaching, classroom activity, coursework and examinations from what pupils have experienced at GCSE level – or, for that matter, in the National Curriculum. The Cockcroft Report noted how easily A-level mathematics teaching could rely on exposition by the teacher, allowing students to develop a passive style of learning. Yet it is important for students in the sixth form to develop problem-solving techniques, to pursue investigations and to discuss and communicate their ideas. Work by Rouncefield (1989) and Kitchen (1989) suggests realistic ideas for projects and practical investigations at this level in statistics and mechanics respectively. Three publications by the Association of Teachers of Mathematics (ATM 1984–8) also provide a lot of starting-points for investigational approaches to a variety of A-level topics.

Two closely related issues are the place of computer work in A-level mathematics and the appropriateness of the emphasis given to calculus as the pure mathematics core at A-level. A lot of practising mathematicians spend much of their time using computers to solve problems, and numerical techniques for obtaining possible solutions are often at least as important as analytical methods. These trends are not reflected by the traditional A-level syllabus.

The question of the future of calculus is discussed by Tall (1987) in a thought-provoking article which recognises the likelihood of major change. Predicting the outcome of such change is perhaps foolish: Tall asks whether calculus is about to stride purposefully in new directions, or quietly fade away and die. Many of the ideas around which calculus is built – limits, continuity, differentiation and integration, rates of change, turning points and so on – are important in mathematics itself and in the development of mathematical models for application. But the vast plethora of techniques, emphasised even more in American calculus courses than in Britain, is in large part potentially supplantable by computer methods. The most productive approach may well be to attempt to synthesise the fundamental ideas of calculus with awareness and experience of related computer facilities. Tall himself has gone some way in this direction by producing the *Graphic Calculus* range of software.

Chapter 8

Professional aspects of mathematics teaching

TEACHER ROLES AND TEACHING STYLES

The role which teachers in secondary classrooms fulfil invloves considerable variation; but, at least for the specialist mathematics teacher, much of this role is determined by school policies and established practice rather than by individual preference. A role which might be labelled 'traditional' involves the teacher in planning material, presenting this in predigested form in a short expository phase in the early part of a lesson, and then setting the class to work on an exercise which reinforces and tests their understanding of what has been said. This exercise may have been devised by the teacher and presented as a worksheet or (usually less effectively) displayed on a board or overhead projector; more often, however, it will be taken from a textbook or scheme. While the class work, the teacher may walk round answering questions, or prompting pupils to work more assiduously. If it becomes clear that a lot of pupils are unable to complete some aspect of the work without help, the teacher may choose to stop the class and make a short announcement to clarify this before the pupils resume work. Also, the teacher may mark the work as the pupils go along, or collect it in at the end of the lesson, or mark it at a later date especially if homework is set.

This brief description of a lesson is so familiar as to be almost a caricature of mathematics teaching. We could all add embellishments to make it more credible and more picturesque. Yet it represents a narrow understanding of mathematics lessons in schools.

For one thing, many schools have in recent years developed individualised learning systems – schemes which allow pupils to work at their own level and their own pace. In such a system, pupils in the same class work on a wide variety of different tasks and topics, and there is no scope for expository teaching. The teacher may act as a facilitator, ensuring that the organisation aspects of the scheme work smoothly, handling pupils' difficulties as they arise, marking work, checking progress and keeping records.

In an investigation-based lesson, the predetermined input may be very sparse, allowing pupils to suggest what questions should be asked, pose their own problems and construct their own strategies. If the whole class is working on the same material, the teacher's function may be to orchestrate the activity, drawing in the ideas of different pupils and promoting discussion and co-operation.

The variation in the behaviour of teachers, and, for that matter, in their expectations of how pupils should behave in mathematics lessons, is recognised by the Cockcroft Report's decision not to indicate a definitive pattern for mathematics teaching. Indeed, the recommendations suggest that classroom practice should provide a variety of modes of teaching and learning for pupils at all levels. Many individual lessons are likely to be consistent in style – this is especially true of individualised, scheme-based work – but, in other situations, a lot of teachers feel that there is value in including different modes of acitivity within the same lesson.

Splitting up a lesson into distinctly contrasting phases can be seen as positive in maintaining interest, or as disruptive of the work. Phases need careful definition. The establishment of modes of working and of the rules for pupil behaviour within those modes is a crucial part of the mechanism of class management and control. A theatrical mode, in which the teacher is the focu , of attention and pupils' contributions are made publicly and with permission, is recognisably different from a mode in which pupils work on exercises, discussing these quietly, while the teacher walks round giving help to those who need it. The transitions from one phase to another become critical points in the lesson, at which experienced teachers give clear cues, indicating to the pupils that this is a moment when the rules change.

While classroom organisations and the teacher's role may be governed by school and departmental policies, there are more personal aspects of teaching which may surface regardless of the context. Thus, in any lesson format, a reflective teacher is more likely to allow space for quiet consideration of ideas and suggestions than one whose inclination is to react quickly and impulsively to any event as it occurs. As another example, some teachers are good improvisers and are able to use the unexpected to good effect and to change the course of a lesson. Those who recognise the weakness of their own improvisation skills may depend more on detailed preparation and be less confident if things do not go according to plan.

Variations in role and style make it difficult to say what makes an individual suited to teaching. Most people with the necessary motivation and academic background appear able to find a style and a context within which they can work; and yet, seemingly inevitably, there are conflicts. An extrovert teacher who enjoys a performance role is likely to be unhappy teaching mathematics entirely in the context of an individualised scheme with no opportunity for class teaching. Such a teacher will try to find ways of interrupting the scheme. A person whose everyday relationships are relaxed and casual may have difficulty adapting in a school whose accepted regime is formal and authoritarian. Similarly, a teacher accustomed to maintaining a sense of authority by keeping pupils or students at a distance will not adjust easily to an institution in which first-name terms and cheerful banter are the order of the day.

Successful teachers may well rationalise their approach, explaining how they teach in a particular style out of conviction that it is appropriate. Others are more self-effacing and will admit that they teach in the only way they can. Some may say that this is about survival, but that is on the whole an overly negative view. At best, the development of an individual teaching style involves personal satisfaction, the growth of an acceptable – and sometimes inspiring – working relationship between teacher and pupils, and the sense of achievement in exploring and appreciating mathematics.

There is, of course, an instability in these matters. Neither teachers nor schools nor fashions stay the same over the years; and recently new structures and demands and guidelines have come thick and fast. Innovations are opportunities or threats, depending how you look at them. Teachers *can* change their styles of working to meet new situations; Nolder (1988) provides a number of case studies. Yet even when the willingness to change is there, and whether the impetus comes from within or without, the process is likely to prove hard for the individual.

Personal teaching habits can become established very firmly and in a relatively short time, especially if the teacher concerned reckons to have found a successful, individual style. Perhaps none of us ever starts from scratch. Those who are strongly motivated to teach mathematics often cite a teacher who influenced their thinking at some stage as their initial inspiration; and a pattern is already there to be imitated. For the newcomer and for the experienced teacher alike, the potential for growth may lie in the ability to conceive of alternatives.

PREPARATION AND PLANNING

The *Non-Statutory Guidance* for mathematics (NCC 1989) offers plenty of advice about preparation and planning. It refers to schemes of work, forward plans and lesson plans. A scheme of work is expected to give clear guidance about the content of work to be covered by a particular age group, as well guidance about the range of teaching styles to be adopted. The guidelines indicate that the order of activities should be flexible, and that the tasks provided for pupils should develop a balance of different types of learning, such as are discussed for example in Chapter 1 of this book. It is also suggested that both independent and co-operative work should be encouraged, and that a variety of modes of learning should be included.

The scheme of work for a key stage in a school has to fit in with the programmes of study, and hence the attainment targets, prescribed by the National Curriculum. Lesson plans, constructed within the scheme of work, depend less directly on the programmes of study. Thankfully, the guidelines do not presume to say how lessons should be planned. They do, however, explain that such plans are formulated in response to more immediate issues, which include considerations of progression and continuity, the needs of individual pupils, and outstanding issues, current interests or questions raised in previous lessons. These remarks are reassuringly (and unimaginatively) uncontroversial.

Of course, despite the protestations of some newly qualified teachers, any initial teacher-training course will tell you how to plan a mathematics lesson. Also, there is no shortage of books which explain what lesson plans should include. A very constructive analysis of the issues involved is provided by Cohen and Manion (1989). On the one hand, intending teachers usually want detailed instructions about this; but, on the other, conflict during teaching practice can be caused by a mismatch between prescriptive demands for lesson plans and the established mode of teaching mathematics in the school. It is worth examining the conventional wisdom of lesson planning, to understand and to recognise how the conflict arises.

The principles on which lesson planning is based usually depend upon what is called an 'objectives model'. This involves specifying the intended learning outcomes in advance, organising the means to achieve these in a rational way, and judging success in terms of the stated objectives. When writers distinguish between aims and objectives, they frequently regard aims as more general, long-term intentions, compared with the more precise, short-term objectives of a particular lesson or series of lessons. Cohen and Manion see the relationship between aims and objectives reflected in that between schemes of work and individual lessons as expressed in this diagram:

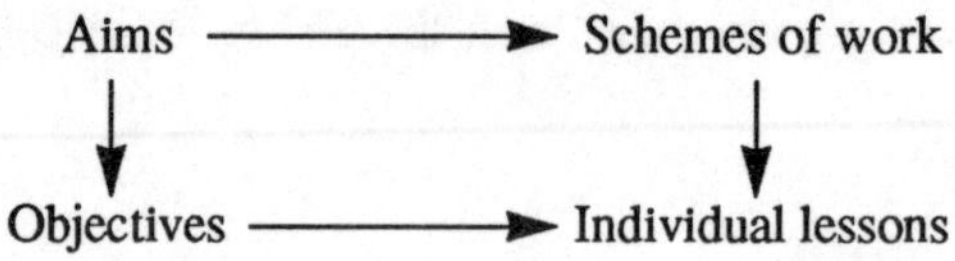

To fit this model, the documentation of a planned lesson should have three components, the first two produced before the lesson and the third afterwards:

- Objectives
- Teaching procedure and classroom activity
- Evaluation

The objectives may be subdivided into behavioural and non-behavioural objectives, the teaching procedure and classroom activity may be planned as a number of phases involving changes of role and style as described in the previous section, and evaluation has a number of aspects to be discussed later. There is some evidence that lesson planning in this format can lead to effective teaching (see Briggs 1970). However, there is a self-fulfilling tendency in all this: an activity which specifies its intended outcomes precisely is more likely to be able to demonstrate its own success.

Nearly all mathematics lessons in some schools, and some mathematics lessons in most schools, can be described sensibly within this model. But there are a lot which cannot, usually for one of two reasons. First, it may be considered entirely inappropriate to assign anything like a common objective to all the pupils in a teaching group; and second it may be thought undesirable, or even impossible, to determine in advance how a non-behavioural objective will be translated into a behavioural objective.

Individualised learning systems, which have grown in popularity for some years, commonly allow and indeed encourage an arrangement in which all the pupils in a class are working on different activities and topics. Such schemes incorporate aims and objectives, which are often made explicit: no doubt publishers will ensure that commercial schemes are shown to meet the requirements of the National Curriculum. The objectives of a particular lesson, however, may be different for every pupil. This does not mean that such systems demand no preparation: on the contrary, teachers need to come to terms with both content and organisational aspects of the scheme. Individualised learning has its own style of evaluation as well, usually involving detailed methods of record-keeping. Yet, in operating such work, teachers do not on the whole determine the objectives or plan the content of lessons, and so any attempt to construct lesson plans within an objectives model is artificial and inappropriate. The implications of this, particularly for student teachers, are discussed in Chapter 10.

In some aspects of mathematical learning, it is easy to express objectives in behavioural terms. As an example, consider the general objective that pupils should understand the place–value principle, applied to three-, four- and five-digit numbers. Indications of success in this respect might be that pupils can do the following:

- Put a set of numbers in order, smallest to largest.
- Add 1 to any number ending in 9 (e.g. 20099).
- Subtract 1 from any number ending in 0 (e.g. 31010).
- Say what the digits 'stand for' (e.g. the 4 in 30407).

A teaching programme can be devised to this end and its effectiveness tested in terms of pupils' performance on these tasks.

In contrast, suppose the general objective is that pupils should be willing to pose their own problems and able to devise strategies for solving these, in a geometrical context. Furthermore, suppose that the classroom activity suggested as a vehicle for this development is that pupils should be given a supply of card hexagons and asked to cut up each hexagon and rearrange the pieces to make a different shape. It might be felt that this suggested objective and activity indicate something of the view of mathematics education held by the teacher or school concerned. The scenario will appeal to some people and not to others. In this context, however, the purpose is not to make a value judgment about how worthwhile an idea this is, but to appreciate the open objective.

While it would make sense to record pupils' behaviour carefully and to analyse later how and to what extent their performance indicated development of the desired characteristics, it would not be appropriate to lay down precise desirable outcomes in advance. Indeed, to do so would be to undermine the spirit of the activity.

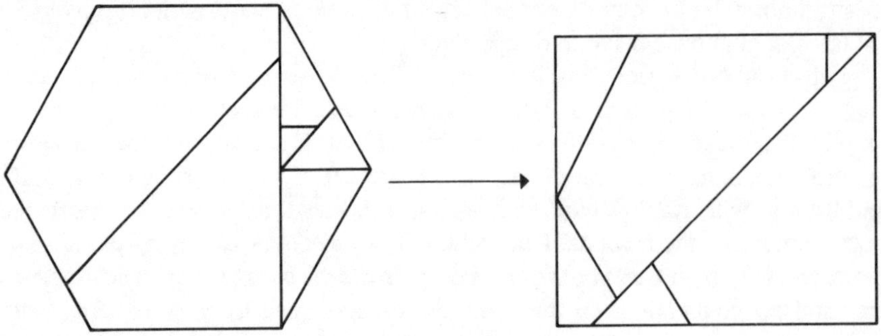

EVALUATION

In the model world, after each lesson, and especially after a series of related lessons, the mathematics teacher reviews the events of the classroom, checks the extent to which the specified objectives have been achieved and makes hypothetical proposals for improvement should the same topic ever be presented to a similar class again. Reality, however, has other pressures, and routine daily evaluation is a neglected aspect of teaching. This is a pity because memories of most lessons soon become blurred, and the potential for development which early reflection can provide is not realised. Half an hour at the end of each working day spent reflecting on each lesson, recognising successes and failures and noting ideas for improvement can pay dividends in terms of awareness of pupils' response, personal satisfaction with teaching, and indeed the smoothness of day-to-day life. At least in the early stages of teaching, it is a worthwhile investment.

The objectives model gives prominence to pupils' performance in specified tasks as an instrument of evaluation. In a successful lesson, pupils acquire the intended competence. But there are other perspectives, and it is possible to distinguish three forms of review which might take place after a lesson:

- assessment of the pupils' performance in the set tasks;
- evaluation of the appropriateness of the material – both the objectives and the activity – for the pupils;
- appraisal of the effectiveness of the teacher, and particularly of the teacher's intervention, in the pupils' learning.

The balance amongst these three aspects and the relative importance of each depend on the role and status of the teacher concerned and the internal and external pressures of the school.

Students on teaching practice, in a school where mathematics is based mainly on an individualised learning scheme, for example, may be:

- required to undertake the first aspect in some standard, predetermined way;
- interested in the second aspect, but forced to push this concern aside, at least for the duration of the practice;
- most immediately concerned with the third aspect, and with the usefulness of their own role.

Of course, a more senior member of staff, or a teacher in a differently organised mathematics department, would have different priorities for evaluation. The implication here is that each should recognise what these are. We can all benefit from a reflective review of our teaching, even if all we do is keep a diary.

RESOURCES, ASSOCIATIONS, JOURNALS AND CONFERENCES

There is no shortage of material to help mathematics teachers decide what and how to teach, or for schools to buy to provide a comprehensive mathematical diet for their pupils. Publishing textbooks and schemes is a lucrative business. No sooner have series been completed to meet the needs of the GCSE examination than these begin to appear in revamped form to satisfy the requirements of the National Curriculum.

The way in which schools use textbooks varies, and there are fashions in this matter: different styles of text become popular. At one stage, school mathematics books were regarded primarily as sources of exercises. The role of the teacher was to introduce topics and explain the methods to be used: only after this activity might pupils be expected to work from the textbook. Some books of this kind are still published, and they have their uses. Others choose to include perhaps one or two illustrative examples before each exercise. It has become normal, however, for texts to include expository material: pupils may be expected to learn mathematics from the book as well as working on exercises which the book provides. Schemes which take this to its logical conclusion may attempt to provide all necessary material for a complete mathematics curriculum.

Another interesting variable is the function of the teacher's book, guide or manual. In some schemes, this is nothing more than a book of answers. Sometimes, it is an annotated version of the pupils' book with notes and solutions. In its most sophisticated form, the teacher's manual may be very much larger than anything provided for the pupils, and contain all kinds of ideas and guidelines for lessons, as well as suggestions of further work and material.

Alongside the trend to publish elaborate schemes and series of textbooks which provide coverage of the curriculum in a neatly packaged way, there has been a very different movement in recent years to develop more open-ended, exploratory material which might encourage a less prescriptive style of mathematics teaching. Much of this reflects the view that pupils can benefit from greater freedom in developing, choosing and appreciating approaches to mathematical situations for themselves, rather than relying entirely on compulsory taught methods. A lot of this is a result of the work of the Association of Teachers of Mathematics (ATM), which has greatly expanded its role in producing teaching resources.

Disconcertingly to most people, there are two quite separate professional associations concerned with teaching mathematics in schools, the ATM and the Mathematical Association. Both provide a lot of information of use to teachers, both publish a range of journals, both have local branches and both hold annual national conferences at Easter time which usually overlap. Individual teachers can become members of these associations, while schools and colleges can have institutional membership. Both associations have concessionary student membership schemes which are very worthwhile. Student teachers are usually (and understandably) reluctant to join both, but an arrangement whereby a few people collaborate to make the material from the two associations accessible to all can work well.

The ATM journals are *Mathematics Teaching* and *Micromath* – a specialist journal concerned with the role of computers in teaching and learning mathematics. The main journals of the Mathematical Association are *Mathematics in School* and the *Mathematical Gazette* – the latter contains more sophisticated mathematics of interest to students and teachers in sixth forms and higher education.

The Mathematical Association is the longer established of the two, and traditionally was more concerned with more advanced mathematics; while the ATM has had a more radical and innovative image. Both associations have broadened their activities, however, with the Mathematical Association validating courses for mathematics co-ordinators in primary schools and the ATM publishing material related to A-level. The styles of the two organisations and of their journals remain distinct, but at the time of writing they appear to be growing closer.

Articles of a more academic nature, describing research in mathematical education, are published in *Educational Studies in Mathematics*, an international journal with considerable British input. The national research group in this field is BSRLM (British Society for Research in Learning Mathematics): the reports of its meetings and conferences provide a reliable picture of current research in Britain. BSRLM is affiliated to an international body (PME) which holds annual conferences.

For many people, however, the most exciting opportunity to discover international aspects of teaching and learning mathematics is provided by the International Congress on Mathematical Education (ICME), held every 4 years in a different part of the world. Thousands of people attend; and for most people, regardless of the value and quality of the conference sessions and activities, being there is the essence of the experience. Some interesting descriptions of and comments on ICME are provided by the collection of articles 'Budapest 1988' in *Mathematics Teaching* (1989).

Chapter 9

Investigations and problem-solving

CURRICULUM DEVELOPMENT IN MATHEMATICS

Curriculum development in Britain has traditionally happened in an unco-ordinated way. Pressures from politicians, the media and employers, the commercial interests of publishers, and the findings of research projects all have their influence on the school curriculum. These forces and others frequently pull in different directions, and the varying importance which people attach to the ideas which bombard them ensures that curriculum change is patchy. The National Curriculum, however, brings some order to the patchwork: it does not totally remove the freedom of teachers to innovate, but it does create a newly restrictive framework within which any innovation must take place.

In spite of the variety, it was possible during the late 1980s for those most aware of developments in mathematics education to claim that some kind of consensus had been achieved. Ernest (1989) writes that 'the mathematics teaching community in Britain is virtually unanimous in its support for a more problem-solving orientation to mathematics teaching, incorporating discussion, practical and investigative work'. This agreement is most evident amongst those involved in research, in writing and in developing innovative resources in mathematical education. At that level, what is published and discussed displays a lot of common ground. For this reason, amongst a relatively small group of people, a particular viewpoint has a high profile and can appear closer to unanimity than it really is.

In a large proportion of schools, mathematics lessons show little evidence of an open, problem-solving orientation; and the National Curriculum requirements, while not precluding such an approach, are constructed in a form which does not encourage it. Some may feel that, through 30 years of research and development, a modicum of success has been achieved in our understanding of what constitutes good practice in teaching and learning mathematics. Yet those involved have failed to communicate this effectively, and have been politically inept in their inability to influence public opinion. The only apparent general agreement is that it is desirable to work towards a better educated and more mathematically competent nation. Activists in mathematics education might argue that we now know a lot about the strategies which might promote this aim, but that schools and teachers have been slow to take new ideas on board, so that little progress is evident. Politicians, however, can claim that years of time-consuming research and experimentation have had little effect, and that some external control is now needed to restore confidence and establish standards.

Expressed in these terms, the debate is simplistic; but, worse than this, it fails to recognise the conflicting premises upon which arguments can be based. It is difficult to separate the teaching methods adopted in mathematics from the kind of competence in the subject which is thought desirable. Because of this, much discussion appears to assume a vision of what mathematical competence means and to focus on the different means which might produce this. Thus Ernest (1989) talks about the 'styles necessary for effective mathematics teaching', and, in a short section entitled 'New Curricula', identifies the shift from text-based whole class teaching to individual study from published schemes as perhaps the greatest change in the teaching of mathematics in 30 years.

Considerations of style are important, and the particular shift to individualised schemes is significant enough to merit a chapter to itself; but, in whatever form the material is presented or taught, there are differences amongst curricula at a deeper level than this. These differences are in the view of what being good at mathematics involves: it is the vision itself which varies, and not just the means chosen to attain it.

The new projects and syllabuses of the 1960s, often described as modern mathematics, exhibit some variety of approach and presentation. Yet they have a recognisable common theme in that they represent a change in emphasis from learning factual information and performing skills in standard ways to developing awareness of the conceptual structures of mathematics. The School Mathematics Project (SMP), in its earliest (numbered) series (in many ways the archetype of such schemes), makes these intentions explicit in the preface to *Book 1* (1965, metric edition 1969), which states that 'these texts pay more attention to an understanding of fundamental concepts' and that 'the difference ... is most marked ...in content'.

In texts and syllabuses produced around this time, the abstract structures of mathematics were identified explicitly, rather than assumed to be part of the underlying growth in pupils' awareness. Thus, work was included on arithmetic in non-decimal bases, not because of any intrinsic importance or usefulness accredited to this, but in the belief that such work can promote a clearer understanding of place–value notation than can the over-familiar processes in base ten. Similarly, the language and notation of set theory was developed in some detail, so that mathematical structures might be described explicitly with greater precision. The first two chapters of *SMP Book 1* give considerably more attention to these themes than would now be considered appropriate.

The change in emphasis to a different learning outcome, which curriculum development projects of the 1960s encouraged, led to some polarisation of intent amongst mathematics teachers, reflected, whether consciously or otherwise, in their classrooms. Skemp's (1976) analysis of relational and instrumental understanding is a distinctive perception of this polarisation. We are not talking (he claims) about better teaching and worse teaching of the same kind of mathematics: rather, there are two effectively different subjects being taught under the same name, 'mathematics'.

While the expressions of unease which led to the setting up of the Cockcroft Committee of Inquiry were at least in part a reaction to the pace of curriculum change, the Cockcroft Report itself did not in any way advocate retrenchment. Rather, by taking on board the identification of different aspects of mathematical learning and setting out the implications of these for classroom practice, the report paved the way for a further broadening of the curriculum. If the reforms of the 1960s shifted the emphasis from facts and skills to an understanding of conceptual structures, the blueprint which Cockcroft provided for the 1980s, by calling for problem-solving and investigational work, encouraged activities through which pupils might learn to create their own mathematical strategies.

The Cockcroft Report spells out investigational work quite clearly, and gives investigation some emphasis by devoting several paragraphs to the idea. No doubt this gave impetus to this kind of mathematical activity, but it scarcely explains the rapid growth in popularity of 'investigations' during the 1980s. There are, after all, plenty of other Cockcroft recommendations which have had little or no effect. Yet investigations have become an established part of school mathematics, and have taken on a somewhat institutionalised form. Presumably, other pressures have encouraged this development.

A clear factor in this has been the coursework requirement of GCSE mathematics. The legitimising effect of GCSE in making investigations respectable is well documented. Nolder (1988) provides several specific illustrations. Andrews (1989) describes the introduction of investigations in the context of GCSE coursework, and Lerman (1989) writes that investigations are becoming a compulsory part of the teaching of mathematics through their inclusion in GCSE mathematics.

It is also possible for teachers to introduce investigations as a means of varying the style of mathematics lessons. Especially when classes are based largely on an individualised scheme, an investigation can be an appropriate way of providing a whole class lesson, in which pupils can come together in discussing a mathematical situation or problem. In contrast, it may also be a way of including group activity and discussion in a situation where mathematics is commonly taught in a more formal, didactic style.

MATHEMATICAL INVESTIGATIONS

If the priority suggested in the previous section is accepted, then an 'investigation' has to allow scope for pupils to devise strategies of their own for working on the problem or within the situation.

Consider these two examples:

(a)

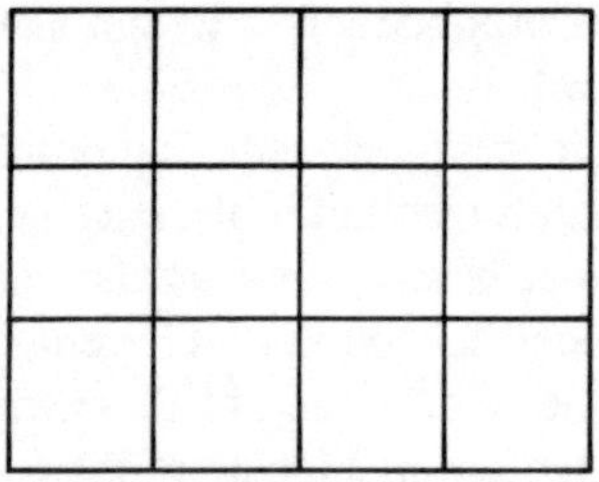

How many squares are there in this figure?

How many rectangles?

(b) Start with any number, and make a chain.

6 3 10 5 16 8 4 2 1 4 2 1 ....

The rules are:

- if the number is even, divide by 2.
- if it is odd, multiply by 3 and add 1.

Does every chain end 4 2 1 4 2 1 ....?

Each of these is presented as a problem – a specific question. Investigations need not be so well defined as this. Pirie (1987) suggests four different methods of presentation:

- a question to answer and a direction on how to start;
- a bald statement which needs to be translated into a problem;
- an explicit question with examples;
- a vague question which leaves the examples wide open.

Her illustrative examples give a clearer idea of each category, although it is difficult – and probably inappropriate – to try to make the classification precise. In practice, the presentation does not always indicate the flavour of the investigation particularly well. The characteristics and potential of an investigation are better identified by asking a number of questions:

- Is it easy to start playing with the situation?
- Does it leave scope for the invention of individual strategies?
- Is there a specific answer to the problem as worded – or a generalisable answer?
- Does the problem suggest other related questions?

Both the examples given above are easy to begin – there is no problem in starting to count the squares, or do the simple arithmetic which the chain demands. Again in both cases, chosen strategies may vary. The squares and rectangles can be counted in various ways, and some may find it useful to begin with a square grid rather than a rectangular one. In the number chain work, decisions may be made about what numbers to try, how to show all the results systematically and whether there is any way of working backwards.

Question (a) has a specific, correct numerical answer in the form in which it is stated. A 'solution' for a general rectangular grid can be expressed in a lot of ways. A rule or counting procedure can be described in words. The number of squares or rectangles may be expressed as the sum of a sequence; and it might be possible to write this sum as a formula by making use of knowledge about the sums of natural numbers and their squares. There are other, more sophisticated approaches. For example, each district rectangle is defined by two vertical and two horizontal lines, and so may be identified by choosing these from the grid:

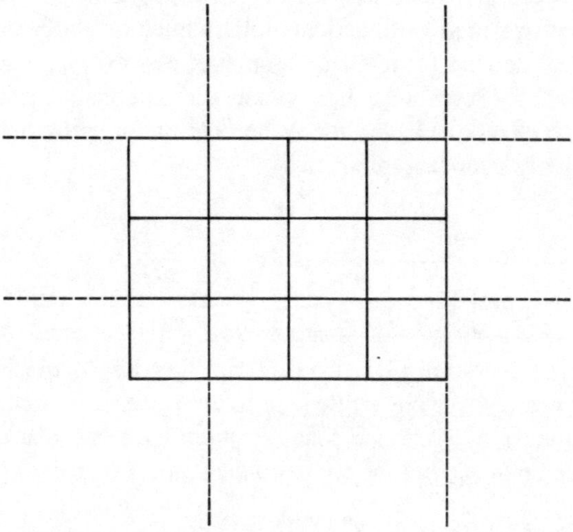

Thus the number of rectangles can be written in combinatorial form as

$$ {}^5C_2 \times {}^4C_2 = 10 \times 6 $$
$$ = 60 $$

Of course the appropriate kind of solution for individual pupils depends on their level of understanding and their perception of the problem. The difficulty for teachers who may know and like a particular answer or approach is that it is tempting to lead pupils to this and impose a way of thinking.

The number chain (b) does always lead to 4, 2, 1..., at least as far as is known, and that means for numbers up to many thousands. It is an interesting level of truth: many pupils are soon convinced that this always happens, and yet there is at the time of writing no proof of this.

Both these problems can be extended. The grid of squares can be replaced by some other pattern; and in the number chain the rules can be altered.

The word 'investigation' is used to describe a whole range of open activity in which the strategies for working are not prescribed. Some writers have tried to distinguish between investigation and problem-solving, but this semantic nicety is somewhat futile: almost any mathematical exercise can be called an investigation if it is presented in the right way. Pirie gives us a clear statement of some things which an investigation is not: it is not a task with a prescribed route to a single solution and it is not an exercise with the overt intention of repetitiously practising a mathematical skill. The emphasis is on exploring, and it is the exploration rather than an 'answer' which is important.

Investigations need not relate to specific topics or subject content in the mathematics curriculum. At a pinch, it might be argued that the rectangular grid problem could be an introduction to sums of sequences or even to combinations. Similarly, the number chain could provide a context in which pupils might be motivated to practise and improve their arithmetical skills, either mentally or using a calculator. These are somewhat far-fetched arguments, however, and it is clear that the initial objectives for presenting these situations to pupils are not of this kind. Many popular investigations have little or no bearing on particular mathematical topics. A commonly seen example is 'frogs':

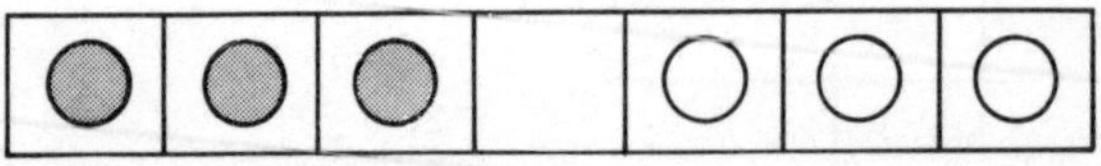

Numbers of black and white counters are placed on a strip like this. A black counter may slide one space or jump over one white counter into a vacant space. In the same way a white counter may slide one space or jump over one black counter. Can you get the black counters and the white counters to change ends? Explore this problem.

Perhaps this is all that should be said. If you have not met frogs before, try it. Sometimes, it is presented as a party game with people sitting on chairs and a vacant chair in the middle. Also there are computer programs which allow you to play the game on the screen. Whether or not you can solve the problem, set yourself some questions about the situation and try to answer them.

Below are some ideas which might be considered.

- Devise a way of recording moves, and keep a record of your procedure.
- Can you find the minimum (or the only, or a possible) number of moves?
- What is the pattern of moves in terms of black and white counters (or left and right movements)?
- Can the pattern be expressed in terms of the type of move, jump or slide?
- How does the vacant space 'move'?
- What about different numbers of counters, and unequal numbers of counters?

The presentation first suggested here is more open than that sometimes given to pupils. Classes may be asked specific questions, like those listed above, or even given a method for recording moves. There is a balance between suggesting the problem in such a way that its potential is unrecognised, and being so dogmatic about what should be done with it that inventiveness is stifled. Judgment about this matter is probably the main feature of good practice in introducing investigations in the mathematics classroom.

Pirie's treatment of investigations is particularly useful, both as a guide to the underlying principles and assumptions and in providing a whole range of situations for the classroom; but there are plenty of other sources, and some schemes incorporate investigations within their published material. The *Points of Departure* series, produced by the Association of Teachers of Mathematics, is an enormous collection of ideas for investigations. Inevitably, individual teachers will find some of these more appealing than others, but most can be used (or adapted for use) with any age or ability level. The form of presentation needs to be considered and modified to suit the particular situation: sometimes more precise instructions will be appropriate, but in some cases teachers may choose to provide greater openness by making their instructions deliberately less than precise.

Some importance is usually attached to bringing together the work on an investigation. If it is intended to be an opportunity for a whole class to work on the same problem, then it is sensible to have a plenary discussion, in which individuals or groups of pupils explain what they have discovered to the rest of the class. Another common way of rounding off work on an investigation is to set pupils the task of writing up their findings. Sometimes this may be a necessary evil for assessment purposes, although it can be seen as a genuinely worthwhile way of developing written communication skills. For some pupils, it will be an unfamiliar task, so that it is important to talk about it first. If pupils have worked on the problem in small groups, it is a useful exercise in co-operation to ask for an agreed report on the activity from each group.

It is worth noting that writing up an investigation can be something very different from setting out a mathematical solution. If the emphasis is on exploring rather than on the answer, then the write-up should reflect this. Without being prescriptive, the guidance offered to pupils to start them on this might involve questions such as the following:

- Describe the situation or problem – what is it all about?
- How did you begin? What did you say or write or do?
- Did any interesting ideas come about? What helped you or made you realise what was needed? What questions did you ask?
- Did you discover anything in particular? A rule or a pattern?
- How do you know you are right? Why does it work?

In this work, persuading pupils to talk amongst themselves and to write down what they say is sometimes quite a breakthrough. Some may be used to writing only the symbols and numbers about which they feel reasonably sure in mathematics: the description of the process and of the uncertainty demands a less inhibited attitude.

An alternative – and in some ways more sophisticated – approach to writing up an investigation is to keep a record of everything as you do it, rather than reflect on and write about it afterwards. Pirie describes this as a form of structured recording. There is no doubt that having to keep a coherent record of your work on a mathematical problem as you go along can be valuable. It provides you, and anyone who looks at the work, with greater awareness of the thinking processes involved, and helps to focus attention on the difficulties and unresolved questions. On the other hand, particularly if the investigation is based on some practical objects such as counters on a board, the demand for a written record can be frustrating to those who find this aspect difficult, and may weaken their motivation towards the activity.

Like the decision about how to present an investigation, the requirements about when and how it should be written up are matters determined by teachers on the basis of their knowledge about their pupils. In both situations, some pupils need more detailed guidance and some can cope with greater freedom. In looking for patterns or rules, some pupils will readily devise systematic ways of tabulating their results while others may need a hint to do this. Relatively few pupils are likely to decide to display their findings in graphical form unless this is specifically encouraged; and yet this is often helpful in appreciating what is going on. Gentle and judicious prompting is part of the process, provided that it does not remove the scope for creative thinking; and responding to a question with another question can be a useful technique.

GUIDED DISCOVERY

Much of the rhetoric of investigations, as reflected in the previous section, shies away from anything which might focus on a specific mathematical skill or structure. Thus the solution has less priority than the strategy which produces it, and pupils are encouraged to develop the work in directions chosen by them. The interspersion of lessons labelled 'investigations' amongst other lessons in which specific mathematical topics are taught and learned, or amongst sessions spent working on an individualised scheme, may create a somewhat distorted view that investigation is a separate aspect of mathematics. While it is true, however, that developing pupils' ability to invent their own strategies is a distinct general objective of mathematical education, the investigational approach has value and applicability in many situations where the objective is specified more narrowly in terms of a particular skill or idea.

Pirie (1987) includes a chapter on investigations which focus on a particular topic: the subjects include area and perimeter, fractions, square numbers and Pythagoras' theorem. Sometimes such activity can be channelled very directly to a particular discovery. The use of dotted or squared paper in investigating the squares on the sides of right-angled triangles is a clear example:

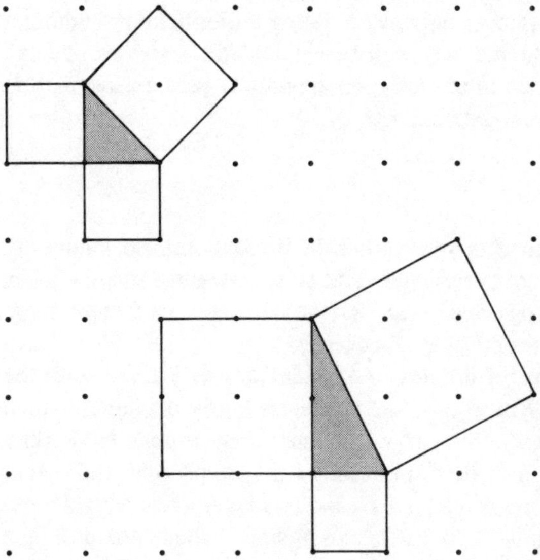

Draw some small right-angled triangles.
Draw squares on each of their sides. Some are easy; others need a little thought and care.
Look for patterns. Think about the areas of the squares; again some are more difficult to work out. Make tables of results.

This has a lot of the flavour of an investigation, but it has a very definite intention. In the plenary discussion, the teacher will no doubt bring together the findings of pupils and groups of pupils in a general statement of the result, which, it is hoped, all will be able to accept.

A subject commonly treated in this style is the relationship between the diameter and circumference of a circle and the value of π. Pupils may measure the dimensions of tins and other cylinders, using string and rulers. The results are recorded in a table, and usually in graphical form as well, and the pupils are guided to a specific conclusion. There are plenty of situations in which it is the development of a practical, investigative approach that is interesting without being particularly difficult. Try, for example, to describe a way of enabling pupils to find out how to calculate the areas of triangles.

If, rather than attempting starkly contrasting styles in different mathematics lessons, we want to work towards some synthesis (or compromise, depending on how you look at it) in our teaching approach, then the demands of the National Curriculum present a number of challenges. What about the requirement that pupils should '... use non-calculator methods by which a three-digit number is multiplied by a two-digit number ...'? Here is a very specific objective. Some may choose to teach the standard long multiplication algorithm. Other, more imaginative teachers may say that this does not have to mean long multiplication, and will devise some procedure which emphasises the place–value structure, or the distributive law of multiplication over addition, or some other concept thought to be important. Yet, it is quite possible to allow pupils to come up with their own strategies. The technique might be to explain that this is something we have to do, and ask for suggestions to be discussed and tried. In a lesson devoted to discovering ways of doing multiplication without a calculator, the most useful resource may well be a calculator – so that you can see whether your method works. In this way, an apparently prescriptive skill is moved into the category of investigational activity.

GAMES

Almost anything can be described as a game. For the present purpose, games are situations in which two or more people play and someone wins: this excludes activities such as solitaire, frogs and most pure mathematics, although these might all be referred to as games in some other context.

From 1986 to 1989 a series of articles in *Mathematics in School*, with the general title 'Maths Games Workshop', suggested all kinds of games which might be used in the mathematics classroom. In one of these articles, Kirkby (1989) attempts a classification of these in terms of their objectives, reflecting the learning objectives of mathematics. A more fundamental distinction, however, is simply to recognise two categories: games which are designed specifically to teach or practise or test or reinforce some particular skill or structure in mathematics, such as co-ordinates or multiplication, and those which have no such content objective but are worth including for their own interest and their potential for developing mathematical strategies.

Games in the latter category are usually presented as investigations. It is necessary to play these games a few times in order to understand the rules, but the interest lies not so much in winning a particular game as in discovering the winning strategy – and then either explaining this or keeping it secret until another player realises what is happening. Some of the ATM Points of Departure are games of this kind; and there are quite a number to be found in the books by Bolt (1982, 1985, 1987). Kirkby suggests an example for two players:

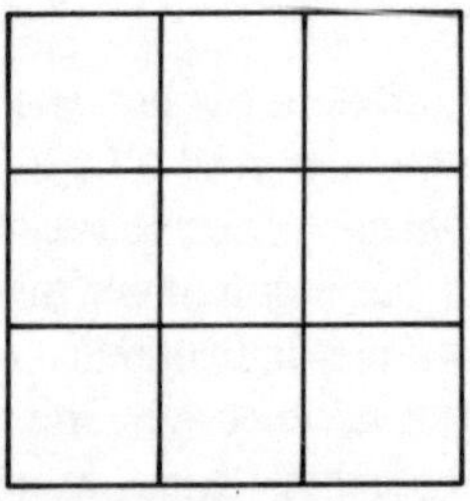

Take turns to place one, two or three counters on the griddle. If two or three are used then they must go in the same row or the same column. The player who places the last counter wins.

Here, only a few games may be needed to find out what is happening, and then the activity becomes an investigation. Can the first player or the second player force a win? How can the rules be changed? What if the last player *loses*? What about differently sized or shaped grids?

A lot of games, even those designed with specific mathematical content in mind, have elements of strategy. Thus a version of battleships might be used, to teach co-ordinates, or some four-in-a-row game with positions given by co-ordinates. In such cases, winning demands not only knowledge of the system but the ability to think of good strategies. Removing the strategy element completely (commonly referred to, in the language of playing games, as 'skill') usually means introducing an element of chance, using dice or cards. A co-ordinate game could be the following.

Players throw two dice in turn. The score on the red die is the x co-ordinate and that on the blue die the y co-ordinate. The point obtained is marked on a grid:

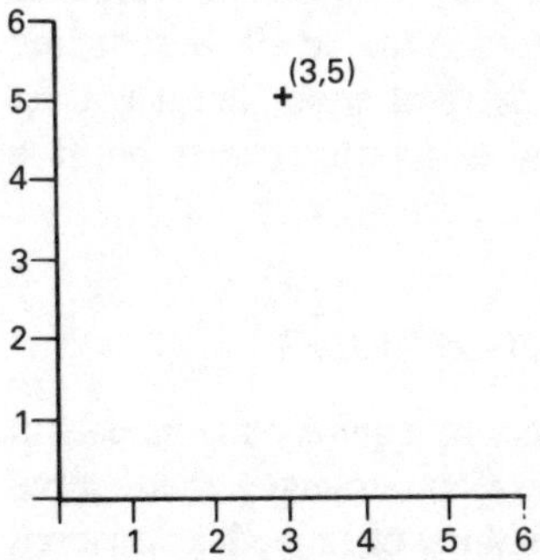

The winner is the first player to produce four points in a straight line.

This is nearly like Kirkby's 'Four Points', although in that version players each have their own grid. There are lots of possible variations of the rules, but (at least provided that a win is recognised when it arrives) this game depends on chance.

It is possible to think of games which demand knowledge and accuracy and where mistakes are penalised. In one version of 'buzz', a group of people are arranged in a circle and then they count in turn round the circle, 1, 2, 3, 4, ... except that any number divisible by 5 or 7 (say) must be replaced by the word 'buzz'. There are innumerable variations: any well-defined category of numbers will do as buzz numbers. Anyone who makes a mistake or hesitates too long is 'out'. This requires an understanding of the rules and quick thinking, rather than the careful construction of a strategy which is more characteristic of an investigation game.

The large number of articles on games in journals and in books of ideas for teachers testifies to the belief that games have a useful place in school mathematics. Dunford (1982) discusses this, noting that games can provide enjoyment, increase understanding and broaden the scope of mathematics. This is really a statement of faith: it is less easy to point to good evidence of the effectiveness of games as a vehicle for learning mathematics.

Some relatively simple strategy games lead to rich investigations, but in these the competitive emphasis is low – it is just a starting point. In games of chance which demand mathematical knowledge or understanding, the motivation to develop this understanding is that without it the game cannot normally be played at all. Games which remain competitive, however, so that better understanding of some mathematical idea will give a greater chance of winning, are presumably based on the assumption that the desire to win is motivating. This is a little dangerous. It is not clear just how motivating the competitive urge is, or that it is desirable to encourage it.

There is some place for games in learning mathematics, and there is no shortage of related resource material and suggestions. It must be recognised, however, that competitive games in particular will appeal greatly to some children – and some teachers – and much less so to others. In daily life, there are people who like card games, for example, and who play with the motivation to win. There are also those who would not be interested in this at all. Introducing some games into mathematics provides a useful variety of style, and it will no doubt motivate some children who would otherwise be less interested, but it is not a guaranteed recipe for success.

REAL PROBLEMS AND MATHEMATICAL MODELLING

Most investigations are based on shapes or numbers in a purely mathematical context. Sometimes, however, the desire to develop strategies and solve problems arises from a real situation. It may be something of immediate concern to us, or it may be a situation about which we are merely curious; but the mathematics which arises is worthwhile if it enables us to understand and describe the situation more clearly and to answer questions about it.

Selkirk (1982), for example, offers a number of starting points for mathematical modelling exercises based on maps or diagrams. The map shows a large village, with about 8,000 population. It has a main post office and a sub post office, each marked PO, and a number of other post-boxes each marked x. The scale is not very accurate, but the distance covered by the map from north to south is about 1.5 km.

In this situation, we can ask all kinds of questions. Why are the post-boxes distributed like this? How far are people expected to walk to post letters? Who goes where? Can the arrangement be improved? Given a map of another large village or small town, we might try to apply the same model, decide where we might expect to find post-boxes, and make comparisons.

While this particular exercise in mathematical modelling is in a familiar context, it does not result (usually) in decisions about actions to be taken. The view that, at least sometimes, school mathematics should involve making decisions and acting on them leads to a different style of real problem-solving.

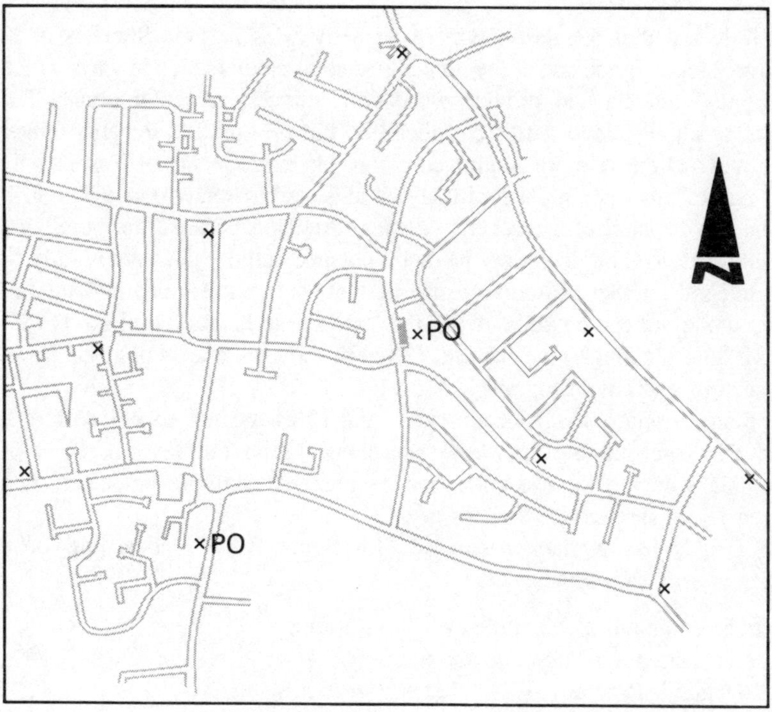

Woods (1988) describes such work in a special school for children with learning difficulties: the two projects described involved planning an outing and building a pond. These are fairly commonly quoted examples.

The idea that a consideration of real projects which can be put into practice is an appropriate part of secondary mathematics is not new. The *SMP Book 1* (1965, metric edition 1969) quoted earlier has a section entitled 'Real arithmetic', which contains a number of examples such as:

- How much does it cost to keep a dog or a cat?

and

- A room is to be turned into a dormitory. Write down the questions you will have to answer before you can work out how many children it will accommodate.

More recently, Burkhardt (1981) provides a rationale for mathematical modelling in the school curriculum, and suggests various approaches. There are teachers with some considerable commitment to work of this nature, but it cannot be said to have achieved general acceptance. For the most part, mathematical modelling in schools remains the preserve of a small number of enthusiasts.

FILLING TIME

It is a little sad that the description of an activity as a 'time-filler' is often pejorative. Making good use of the time allocated to mathematics in ways which retain pupils' interest and provide worthwhile experience is important. The length of a school lesson varies considerably, but the trend is towards longer periods, and an hour or more is quite common. There are plenty of reasons why a small part of this time might profitably be allocated to something different. It might be the decision of a teacher to change direction because the pupils are losing motivation. It might simply be that a planned activity does not readily fit into an integral number of hours. It may be that some pupils need a change of activity, while others continue with the earlier work. As Dunford (1982) remarks a little scathingly, the class may even be reduced to a small group by an epidemic of measles or a geography field-trip.

These are normal enough occurrences, and ideas are not to be scoffed at because they are suitable for these occasions. Quite the reverse. It is of considerable value to have a collection of prepared activities to meet such contingencies, at short notice if necessary.

Pirie (1987) has a chapter entitled '15-minute fillers', consisting of a collection of problems which:

- can be communicated in no more than 2 minutes;
- can be started in at least one obvious way;
- allow pupils to achieve something within 15 minutes.

There are lots of other sources. Many of the items, particularly the puzzles, in Bolt's books could be put into this category. So might some of the ATM *Points of Departure*, although these need choosing carefully and sometimes defining more explicitly. Crosswords, cross-number puzzles, magic squares and some dissection puzzles are useful. Many such problems are suitable for any age group, but personal interests and experience will guarantee that every teacher will have different favourites and produce a different collection.

Chapter 10

Mixed-ability teaching and individualised learning

MIXED-ABILITY GROUPING

The spread of mixed-ability grouping arrangements in secondary schools is an extension of one of the principles of comprehensive education. If it is inappropriate to select children for different schools on the basis of educational achievement at the age of 11, then it is also unwise at that age to divide them into streams or sets within the school on a similar basis.

There is nothing extraordinary about mixed-ability classes. Primary schools have always grouped children of a range of ability together, and indeed many small and medium-sized schools will have no more than one class in each year group. In smaller schools a class may cover a broader age range than 1 year, but grouping by age is the normal practice in Britain. There are vertically grouped primary schools with mixed age and ability in each class, but these are relatively unusual. Forming classes of homogeneous ability regardless of age is virtually unknown.

The most common strategy adopted by teachers in primary schools is to arrange the seating in the classroom so that children of a similar level of attainment work together. As explained in Chapter 7, there is no real evidence that such a grouping arrangement has any bearing on the effectiveness of the learning, but it may make it easier in organisational terms for the teacher to set appropriate work. This strategy has not been copied in many secondary mathematics classes, where small group work is relatively unusual.

The increased awareness in recent years of the enormous differences in children's level of attainment in mathematics has led many teachers to question the value and practicality of teaching the same material to all pupils in a mixed-ability group. The work discussed in Chapter 1 on children's understanding of the place–value system was quoted in the Cockcroft Report as an illustration of the 7 year gap. Some 7 and 8 year olds can cope with questions which demand this understanding, while a sizeable minority of 14 and 15 year olds cannot do so. From a different viewpoint, this means that a mixed-ability group of 11-year-old children may contain some whose level of sophistication in mathematics compares with the average of 7 year olds, while others are as competent as most 14 and 15 year olds. Realising this allows teachers to recognise a disparity amongst the children which is not obvious from their appearance.

Some other topics can be even more disquieting. The APU data on finding the area of a triangle, quoted in Chapter 4, is confused by the variations in language and presentation, but there is enough consistency in it to discuss the implications for teaching. Leading pupils to find the areas of triangles by fitting them inside rectangles is a common enough part of secondary mathematics teaching. Yet it appears that about half of all pupils understand and can cope with this when they leave primary school at the age of 11, and that a substantial proportion of the remaining half are never going to grasp this principle during their secondary school careers. So, to whom is this teaching directed? Teachers who spend time introducing this topic to a whole, mixed-ability class are providing useful learning for perhaps a handful of pupils. The argument is a bit simplistic, but it is sufficiently justifiable to be taken seriously.

Many of the problems and the opportunities of mixed-ability teaching are still there when classes are set by ability: but mixed-ability arrangements bring increased awareness. It is notoriously difficult to produce reliable assessment procedures to construct sets by ability, and even pupils of comparable ability may vary greatly in their pace of working and in their understanding of individual topics. In many ways, this variation is at least as significant as difference in ability when all pupils are expected to complete the same work.

INDIVIDUALISED LEARNING SCHEMES

Doubts about class teaching as a way of working with mixed-ability groups have led in recent years to the increased use of individualised learning schemes. These schemes may be based on a system of booklets, workcards, worksheets or a mixture of these. Pupils work at their own level and their own pace, so that all may be working on different topics or activities and, in theory at least, some may be years ahead of others. In practice, the order of the work has some flexibility, and is not devised as a linear progression. Careful planning and organisation is required, and, perhaps even more careful record keeping.

The SMP 11–16 scheme is the most popular individualised system, and in some parts of the country completely dominates secondary mathematics. The booklet scheme, with its support for mixed-ability grouping, is used only in the lower years of the secondary school, however. For work leading to GCSE examinations, SMP 11–16 changes style and direction completely with a series of textbooks, colour-coded for different levels of ability.

Despite its popularity, SMP 11–16 is a relative newcomer in the market. Longer established schemes include the Kent Mathematics Project (KMP), which has undergone a number of revisions. This scheme can provide for the 9–16 age range, and it remains individualised and essentially workcard based throughout. For those committed to this style of classroom organisation, it has its attractions. Also worth mentioning, and in fairly widespread use, is the Secondary Mathematics Individualised Learning Experiment (SMILE).

All these schemes have been planned with some care, so that teachers can expect to find them worthwhile and attractive: they are after all designed for commercial success. They may include a variety of additional material, such as equipment, sets of investigation cards, computer software or other supplementary resources. It all depends what you want.

Inevitably, since the schemes were published some years earlier, the National Curriculum legislation has created a need for change, and publishers have responded to this. Because of the nature of this material, individualised systems have been classified into levels, not necessarily corresponding to age groups. There has been no consistency in the numbering of these levels across different schemes, and they have not matched the levels of the National Curriculum. Some rationalisation will no doubt take place over the next few years.

SIDE EFFECTS OF INDIVIDUALISED LEARNING

During the 1980s, large numbers of secondary schools reorganised the teaching of mathematics, in the lower years at least, to incorporate an individualised scheme. The intended purpose of allowing pupils to work on material at a more appropriate level of difficulty, and at a pace suited to the individual, is a worthwhile one; and, on the whole, teachers appear satisfied that sensible use of individualised learning can promote this. To that extent, this has been a very positive development.

At the same time, any change in the way classes are organised is bound to have other effects as well, which might also be positive, but which need attention. There may be an effect on the relationships between teacher and pupils, and amongst pupils, on discipline, on conversation and dialogue in the classroom and on pupils' attitude to learning mathematics. Widespread though these concerns are, schools' experiences of such change have not been very well documented in the last few years. Although the biggest growth in the popularity of such systems has taken place recently, individualised learning is not a new idea and has been described in articles over 25 years or more. It is perhaps this long-established discussion which discourages people from continued reappraisal of old arguments and issues.

There is some evidence that discipline problems are less likely in classrooms organised on an individualised basis. An early description by Langdon (1976) of the introduction of the SMILE scheme goes so far as to state that 'the old confrontations between class and teacher don't happen any more'.

This is too sweeping a claim; but it is true that the activity becomes very much the pupil's work, and the teacher's role is that of helper rather than authority figure. There are, on the other hand, some teachers who would feel this change of role in itself as a loss of control: experienced teachers inevitably develop their own strategies and mechanisms for maintaining discipline within an established style of working.

Over the years, the most frequent criticism of individualised learning schemes has been that they may reduce the quality of dialogue in the classroom (see for example Romiszowski 1979). The teacher's contribution can degenerate into purely organisational matters concerned with which cards or booklets to work on, what equipment to use and so on. Because pupils are all working on different material, discussion amongst them is unlikely to focus on the mathematics and becomes peripheral to their learning. In this context, learning may cease to be a corporate or co-operative activity. These matters need a little care – it is possible for teachers to promote and generate mathematical discussion with pupils, when working in this way, but it needs a conscious decision to do so.

Some consideration has been given to the adequacy of individualised schemes in meeting the needs of the least able and most able pupils in mathematics. As far as less able pupils are concerned, published schemes vary in their approach. The SMP 11–16 material was not written to cover the entire ability range, and has not been promoted as suitable for the least able pupils, but Ernest and Galvin (1987) report some success in using the scheme with low attainers. The KMP includes material specifically designed for lower attaining pupils.

Using workcard- or booklet-based material with mathematically able pupils has inherent dangers. Pupils can, if they wish, choose to make life easy for themselves, taking the work slowly or adopting an over-relaxed approach. The material, most of which is designed for a broad ability range, may not be especially motivating. It is possible to recognise a long-standing uneasiness about this (see Hytch and Tidmarsh 1969) and enrichment material in various forms may be advocated, whether or not this is included as an intrinsic part of the scheme.

Another concern is the effect of individualised learning on the teacher's enthusiasm. Nolder (1988) quotes the example of one teacher who did not enjoy his early experience with SMILE and whose attitude to individualised schemes was marred by this. As discussed in Chapter 8, there are many teachers who like the performance role and find little satisfaction in acting as a low-profile facilitator. There is something of a dilemma here. If pupils enjoy this style of working and learn effectively through it, then it may be difficult to consider teacher satisfaction as a priority. Fortunately there is plenty of opportunity for teachers to introduce a contrasting way of working in some lessons; and it is common practice in some classes to interrupt individualised systems by including the occasional lesson or series of lessons of an entirely different kind. If work on an investigation, for example, is used in this way, it can provide a variety of style and experience and also allow an opportunity for debate and discussion involving all the class.

Over the years, particular forms of organisation have sometimes been promoted as a partial answer to the shortage of specialist mathematics teachers in secondary schools. A carefully planned scheme, with the learning prescribed in detail and in which pupils learn from the printed material rather from the teacher, might be more 'teacher-proof', so that it might not need the supervision of a well qualified mathematics specialist. Also, it might be imagined that, if pupils are able to learn for themselves from the scheme without teacher intervention, then a teacher could supervise a larger class. The style and organisation of popular individualised schemes, however, have not developed in such a way as to make these expectations realistic.

In some respects, teachers using an individualised system need greater competence and confidence in their own mathematical awareness. They do not plan the content of lessons and they have less control over the topics, questions and examples which might arise during each session. They need to be able to respond to unexpected ideas and problems, and to switch quickly from one topic or situation to an entirely different one. Moreover, pupils' expectations of individual attention from the teacher can be very demanding: many teachers claim that they could always use extra help in individualised lessons and there is no scope for increased class sizes.

In Chapter 13, on attitudes, some consideration is given to how individualised work might affect pupils' emotional response to learning mathematics. Most pupils appear to like working in this way, and some may even resent the interruption of their work by a different style of mathematics lesson. The theatrical style of some traditional mathematics teaching has a spotlight effect which can focus attention on the lack of understanding of individual pupils in a sometimes distressing way. Pupils who report unhappy experiences of mathematics lessons are likely to refer to such situations. The more individualised style can allow such pupils to negotiate their understanding of mathematics without public exposure of their weakness.

In teaching mixed-ability groups, the arguments on cognitive grounds for providing work geared to individual levels of attainment are strong. The other considerations discussed in this section are reasonably encouraging, but a number of reservations and possible modifications can be identified. The implication is that teachers need to be aware of and take account of these matters in deciding on the style of classroom activity.

UNDERSTANDING THE SCHEME, PLANNING AND EVALUATION

As considered in Chapter 8, individual lesson plans based on an objectives model are inappropriate in the context of individualised learning. This is sometimes a cause of consternation to students on teaching practice: it does not make these schemes an easy option. It may well be, however, that a student in training has an advantage over a newly appointed teacher who has to start work within the context of an unfamiliar scheme. To work effectively, teachers need to become acquainted with the content and, even more critically, with the organisational aspects of the scheme. Students usually have the opportunity to do this by working with experienced teachers in the classroom, whereas the newly appointed teacher may find it difficult to arrange this. The essential preparation for teaching mathematics in this way lies in this process of familiarisation.

While individualised learning makes lesson plans inappropriate, it does demand extensive evaluation. This evaluation has various aspects, including the following:

- keeping detailed records of pupils' progress, usually in a format provided by the scheme;
- reviewing, formally or informally, the organisational aspects of the scheme, with a view to possible modification of the classroom arrangements;
- monitoring the development of pupils' attitudes and motivation, and of the working relationships with and amongst pupils, with a view to possible variation of the style of lesson;
- assessing the amount, quality and effectiveness of teacher intervention in the pupils' work and learning.

It can also be useful sometimes for a student or observer or support teacher to follow closely the work of one or two pupils during a series of lessons. The variety of activity in the classroom can appear very busy and complicated and the activity (or, for that matter, the inactivity) of individual pupils can go unnoticed.

For the student or inexperienced teacher in particular, keeping a record of every lesson based on a scheme of this kind is important and valuable. The focus and emphasis given to the different aspects may vary, but the development of good practice depends on reflective evaluation. Again, the most useful approach may be to make diary notes of lessons at the end of each day.

Chapter 11

New technology in mathematics education

CALCULATORS AND COMPUTERS

It is arguable that this chapter should not be a separate chapter at all, that the relevance and use of new technology should be a part of the discussion in every chapter, whatever topic or issue is explored. Equally, it is arguable that calculators and computers should not be lumped together in the same section – that the issues involved are quite different. If mathematics education in schools were being set up from scratch, with new accommodation, new resources and (especially) new teachers, the role of new technology might be very different – and very much more taken for granted. However, schools, teachers and the curriculum already exist, and are as they are for all kinds of historical and personal reasons. New technology is an 'issue' because it is an aspect of curriculum change.

Resistance to curriculum change is discussed in various chapters of this book. Often this is a reaction to innovation, which is seen as too radical and labelled pejoratively as progressive. The use of calculators in schools frequently provokes a popular reaction of this kind, but the use of computers does not. Calculators are somehow perceived as dangerous and leading to lower standards whereas computers are considered important, and schools are praised for providing children with the experience and awareness of computers which they will need in a technological world. Fundamentally, it is this difference in public image and response which makes the issues of computers and calculators different. There are three issues, however, which relate to computers and calculators alike, although not necessarily with equal emphasis in each case.

Firstly, the use of new technology is sufficiently important to be a worthwhile learning objective in itself. Computers and calculators change the way in which mathematics is done and may indeed change the essential nature of mathematics itself. New techniques, structures, notation and language are developed; and, alongside this development, the belief arises that young people should learn about these things. Thus, technological change adds new topics and activities to the school curriculum. In the framework of the National Curriculum, information technology is identified mainly within the 'design and technology' subject area. It is clear, however, that some computer facilities are regarded as part of the mathematics curriculum: spreadsheets, databases, graph-plotting facilities and LOGO are all mentioned specifically.

The second issue is that, while calculators and computers add to the school mathematics curriculum by providing new activities and facilities, they also take away from it by making other skills less important or even obsolete. As discussed in Chapter 2, standard procedures for pencil-and-paper arithmetic now have little utilitarian value. Those who advocate calculator usage may argue with considerable justification that the emphasis given to written arithmetic can and should be abandoned. Yet, popular opinion is stubbornly sceptical on this issue. There is a fear that reliance on calculators will weaken skills and understanding which are necessary for daily life or for further study. In most parts of the world, the use of calculators is not encouraged in elementary schools.

The two issues so far raised are concerned with changes in the spread of objectives in teaching and learning mathematics. New needs arise, and old ones become less significant. At the same time, computers and calculators are aids to teaching and learning; they provide new approaches to topics which remain recognised as essential parts of secondary school mathematics. Alternative approaches to algebra, geometry and statistics become possible, using calculator and computer facilities. Often more realistic problems can be tackled, or more extensive investigational work carried out, because pupils' progress and motivation need not be hindered by difficult or tediously time-consuming arithmetic.

OBSOLESCENT ACTIVITIES

It is easy to see the growth of fresh ideas which new technology can bring to mathematics education in a positive light. Initially, some teachers may feel awed or in danger of being left behind by such innovation, but at least it brings the promise of new interest and stimulation. It is much more difficult to accept the view that other, long-established activities are now less important, and in some cases might not be worth teaching and learning any more.

Fey (1989) provides a survey of developments and of the significant problems involved in using technology in mathematics education. His discussion of the influence of calculators on the objectives of teaching arithmetic includes some useful insights. The enormous weight of research in this area over almost 20 years indicates that sensible, routine use of calculators in school mathematics does not inhibit children's development of more traditional skills, particularly in mental arithmetic. Indeed, when used constructively, calculators can improve conceptual understanding, problem-solving ability and attitudes towards mathematics. For many researchers, the debate is over and the question is answered. It is appropriate to allow and indeed to encourage the use of calculators in school mathematics, and further research will be of interest only if it seeks to determine the effectiveness of new approaches to teaching and learning mathematics with the aid of calculators.

While the studies reported by Fey and others may include situations where calculators have been used extensively, this use has been complementary to a more traditional, albeit often somewhat reduced, programme of computational arithmetic. A more daringly radical approach would be to encourage both mental arithmetic and the use of calculators, but to abandon standard, pencil-and-paper procedures entirely. Such an approach seems politically impossible in Britain at present, and it would certainly be against the spirit of the National Curriculum requirements; and for these reasons its consideration is off the agenda. Established opinion and prejudice is strong in this matter, but rational justification for the emphasis which some teachers give to standard algorithms is more difficult to produce.

There are lots of other topics in mathematics whose value is greatly weakened by technological developments. Logarithm tables and slide rules, for example, are consigned to the historical interest category. Formal algorithms for solving algebraic equations are increasingly replaced by trial and improvement procedures, and analytic techniques which depend on a whole catalogue of methods of differentiation and integration may be less appropriate than numerical methods. In statistics, techniques for coding and simplifying data to make calculations easier are no longer necessary when raw data can be entered and processed quickly. It may even become recognised that some forms of statistical testing have grown historically in a way which was appropriate for manual calculation: computer systems may allow different, more effective procedures to be developed.

All these effects – and many more – will please some people and displease others. Some primary teachers, accustomed to regarding the teaching of standard arithmetical techniques as their main concern in mathematics, will feel that their role is virtually destroyed if this emphasis is removed. Specialist mathematics teachers may find one of their favourite topics removed from the normal curriculum. Certainly, many who teach A-level will be unhappy if the central place of calculus in mathematics syllabuses at their level is diminished.

The direct study of computer technology, which has found a place, for example, in subjects such as 'computer science', is not a part of mathematics; and many mathematicians would not want to put too strong an emphasis on the relationship between mathematics and computing. Yet there is no doubt that computers have changed radically what most professional mathematicians do, whether in an academic or commercial environment. Those who entered teaching some years ago have seen the education system, and frequently their own jobs, change around them; but mathematics graduates of some years standing may also feel that the context and flavour of their subject has changed around them as well.

Fortunately, most teachers are not so introspective nor so self-indulgent as to dwell upon these matters. Teaching demands a certain amount of compromise, and a willingness to recognise constraints which sometimes inhibit change and sometimes enforce change. Above all it demands faith in the future and a concern for the best interests of pupils.

Since the mid-1980s, the Association of Teachers of Mathematics (ATM) has published a journal, *Micromath,* concerned with the use of computers and calculators in mathematics education. Inevitably, almost all the articles in this journal are written by teachers with an enthusiasm for activity of this kind, and are likely to be read by those with similar enthusiasm. There are exceptions: one 'opinion' article by Burrows (1989) describes how one teacher with unfavourable views on technological innovation came to terms with the use of a computer, by recognising just one way in which it could enhance the experience of her pupils. Perhaps more is needed at this level.

COMPUTER TUTORIAL PACKAGES

Some of the earliest ideas for producing computer-assisted learning packages envisaged the computer acting like, and in some way replacing, the teacher. In such a system the computer may introduce topics by providing information and examples on a screen. Questions or tasks are then set for the pupil, whose performance on these tasks determines what happens next. New information may be provided, old information may be repeated, fresh tutorial advice may be offered, or the pupil may be told simply to try again.

This view of programmed learning which was fashionable some years ago has not, on the whole, been translated into widespread production and use of computer software. Other, better integrated and more imaginative ways of using computers in school mathematics have been developed. It is arguable that individualised learning schemes, based on workcards, worksheets or booklets, are the most direct descendants of the programmed learning tradition.

Computer packages exist which attempt to convey substantial parts of the content of school mathematics, and to test knowledge of this work. Such packages are sometimes of little value, unimaginative and extremely expensive. At worst, the information may be displayed on the screen just as if on the pages of a book. It is difficult to see the point of this: it could be presented more effectively, more accessibly and more cheaply in textbook format.

There are a lot of useful and popular programs available, however, which focus on a particular mathematical skill or conceptual structure and provide pupils with relevant experience, practice and reinforcement. Examples have already been quoted in earlier chapters which provide pupils with the opportunity to develop understanding of angle size, of co-ordinate notation and of the lengths of diagonal lines on a co-ordinate grid. Sometimes the activity may be provided in the form of a game: appreciation of the place–value notation, for example, can be fostered by the MINIMAX program (SMILE), which requires digits to be inserted into a calculation to make the answer as large (or as small) as possible.

A brief glance through the contents of recent issues of *Micromath* is sufficient to indicate that the focus of attention has moved away from sharply directed software of this kind. People write about investigations and adventure games, about LOGO and other microworlds, and about facilities such as spreadsheets and graph-plotters and how they use these to do or teach mathematics. Yet, there remains a place for programs with specific and closely defined objectives, related to the understanding of particular mathematical topics. Some provide clever and imaginative settings, and form a valuable addition to the pupils' experience of a topic, whether seen as remedial activity, reinforcement or enrichment. Such use of the computer is apparently considered successful, and will no doubt remain common in schools.

COMPUTER-BASED INVESTIGATIONS AND ADVENTURE GAMES.

Almost any mathematical puzzle or problem can be made into a computer program which sets the scene and allows pupils to investigate a variety of cases before coming to (or failing to come to) a desirable generalisation. Some available programs, such as FROGS (SMILE) as described in Chapter 9, simply provide a way of working on the problem on the computer, as an alternative to using, say, counters or people or pencil and paper. On other occasions the use of the computer sometimes has a distinct benefit, as in the program ROSE (SMILE) which allows all the diagonals of a many-sided polygon to be constructed on the screen much more quickly than they could be drawn on paper. In other cases, the computer provides unknown numbers, rules or patterns, which have to be identified by some sort of investigative strategy. PYXIDIUM (Shell Centre) is one example of this: its use is reviewed by Rahman (1988).

These problem-solving programs, of which there are dozens if not hundreds available, promote the invention of investigative strategies, but the questions asked and the kind of answer required are narrowly channelled by the structure of the program. The most elaborate examples of this type of software are mathematical adventure games. The first such game to become well known and have any extensive use in schools was 'L: A Mathemagical Adventure' (ATM): this was discussed extensively in early issues of *Micromath.* Another well-known example is Martello Tower (Straker), reviewed by Parr (1988).

If investigation programs and adventure games are criticised, it is usually on the grounds that they do not give you much choice about what you do. Nevertheless, people usually enjoy them and impose their own ideas in talking about and negotiating the problems. The message that emerges from most reports of work with such software is that a broad range of activity can develop, sometimes connected to the computer program and sometimes not. Dobson (1988) provides examples of pupils' written work stimulated by TADPOLES (SMILE): this is related closely to the software. It is often the adventure games which generate masses of ideas, particularly at top junior level where these ideas can be the basis of a cross-curricular topic lasting for several weeks.

The value of the resources discussed in this section appears to lie very much in their use as starting points. Their full potential is exploited when there is the opportunity to discuss and follow up the ideas in further and more varied work.

PROGRAMMING IN MATHEMATICS EDUCATION

There have been arguments for some years about whether it is sensible to include a small amount of programming in a computer language such as BASIC in the school mathematics curriculum. The requirements of the National Curriculum do not demand this, although there are various places where it might be useful. In the number/algebra attainment target, a BASIC program is given as an illustration of the level 5 requirement that pupils should follow simple sets of instructions to generate sequences. At level 7, the same attainment target requires the exploration of more complex patterns of number generated by a computer: sufficient programming skill to produce these would be helpful here.

One form of programming frequently advocated is the writing of procedures in LOGO, but this is somehow different. In LOGO, pupils are working in a microworld and defining procedures in a way in which they produce their own new structures in that world. In contrast, BASIC programs are more often written to investigate or solve some problem arising in mathematics in a more effective way.

Price and Price (1988) give an example of the use of a computer to extend the scope of an investigation on magic squares. The discussion illustrates how significant the ability to write a simple BASIC program can be in a mathematical investigation, and how it can affect the level of sophistication of the work generated quite dramatically. At present, work and facilities of this nature are accessible to some pupils from an early age, but not at all to others – and the access may be at school or outside school. In many aspects of problem-solving, investigations, projects and coursework, some programming skill is a clear advantage – both in tackling the problem and in producing an impressive presentation and write-up. Perhaps some pupils are going to be disadvantaged if no experience of this work is provided by the school curriculum.

Whether or not it is important for pupils to learn some BASIC, it is certainly useful on some occasions for a teacher to be able to produce a simple program to help with exploratory and investigational work. Some examples are provided by the Mathematical Association (1985). The book from the same association (1989), *Mathematics Homework on a Micro*, has a self-explanatory title. In spite of its title, however, many of its suggestions are useful as classroom activities. The program FINDING ZEROS, for example, encourages a trial and improvement method of solving algebraic equations, in line with some of the National Curriculum requirements.

The programs listed in both these books from the Mathematical Association are available on disc. The introduction to one book suggests that some teachers may wish to save the programs on disc anyway, so that pupils who are not familiar with computers are saved the labour of typing them in and can concentrate immediately on the mathematical activity involved. There is plenty of scope for differences of opinion here, and you may take your choice.

- Is it valuable for pupils to be able to write simple BASIC programs?
- Is it valuable for pupils to type programs from given listings into the computer?
- Or, if a program is worth using in mathematics lessons at all, is it then worth providing it, ready written and saved on a disc?

One consideration might be that as software becomes more polished and sophisticated its production becomes more magic and mysterious. Perhaps it is worthwhile for pupils to see that useful programs are sometimes quite unpolished, and can be entered in a very simple form.

LOGO AND OTHER MICROWORLDS

For many people, the most appealing function of computers in mathematical education is their potential to allow pupils or students to operate in a microworld. Fey (1989) expresses his own view of the characteristics of a computer microworld. It is a realm in which 'mathematical or real world objects, relations, and operations are represented electronically in ways that permit controlled exploratory manipulation and observation of properties by learners searching to abstract underlying mathematical principles'.

The microworlds which LOGO provides are much the best known, most explored and so far most fruitful of such environments. For this reason, these ideas deserve most attention. It is worth examining some other examples, however, because they are interesting in themselves but also to allow comparison of the features and possibilities of their different landscapes.

A relatively simple microworld, which nevertheless qualifies for inclusion within this definition, is ZOOM (MEP). ZOOM sets up a situation in which it is possible (using the arrow keys) to draw simple diagrams and pictures and to move around the screen. The exciting part is the ability to enlarge or reduce the design by any scale factor and from any centre of enlargement. This can give you the sense of getting inside the picture, or of putting everything you have drawn so far into a much wider setting. Despite its unsophisticated presentation, ZOOM is very popular with some children, and the notes provided with the package include some interesting examples of children's work.

Unlike LOGO, ZOOM has no form of programming: new procedures cannot be created within it. An example of another microworld which allows a form of programming is PLAN (PEG Exeter) which is reviewed by Jones (1988). PLAN allows users to create and play text adventure games. It includes 'buildmode' for writing games and 'playmode' for playing them. Creating structures in PLAN requires a logical form of statement which can be used as an introduction to the micro-Prolog language. PLAN commands, however, have their own particular style, which Jones' discussion shows as accessible to a group of fourth-year secondary school pupils. The situations produced by these pupils very much reflect their own interests: they are amusing, logical and not always in the best of taste.

NUMERATOR (Logotron) is an elaborate microworld. It is a powerful environment in which it is possible to generate, manipulate and process numbers by creating carefully structured models. Its practical if somewhat eccentric format has an attraction all of its own. Ball (1989), reviewing the NUMERATOR package, explains that it has some of the features of a computer language and talks about 'programs'. Yet the essence of its code is visual – perhaps even iconic rather than symbolic. It is difficult to describe the collection of tanks, pipes, processors and so on which are created in NUMERATOR as a 'program': the documentation calls it a 'workspace'. In terms of the flavour of the activity, the workspaces are structures created by plumbing within this particular microworld.

The large manual supplied with NUMERATOR describes some ready-made systems called 'walkthroughs', and several case studies of its use in classrooms. Neither of these features will have universal appeal: there may well be easier and more direct ways of starting work than following the walkthroughs, and the case studies are a little unexciting. The possibilities seem interesting, and yet the suggestions in the manual may not make the most exciting use of the software.

NUMERATOR has a lot of capabilities. It can produce graphs and charts, the workspace can be printed from the screen, and a simple world-processing facility allows diagrams to be labelled and annotated. Many people feel that it has a lot of potential which has yet to be described and explored fully.

The microworlds described so far have a variety of individual and shared characteristics. They have particular uses, but they have nothing like the influence or the fame of LOGO. LOGO comes in various versions, and many new computers have it as part of their inbuilt core software. Interestingly, one of the most useful and entertaining descriptions of LOGO is given in the *Logotron Logo Book* supplied with the Logotron LOGO software. The origins of LOGO, and its roots in Papert's *Mindstorms* (1980), are discussed there, and also in an article by Bunyard (1989). In one sense, the development of LOGO may be seen as a reaction to the programmed learning packages described earlier. Papert is quoted as aiming to 'allow children to program the computer rather than be programmed by it'.

LOGO is usually introduced as a means of giving instructions to a moving robot, called a 'turtle'. Robot turtles may actually be used – they are small machines which move around the floor, controlled from the computer. Otherwise, the instructions given control the movement of a screen turtle – usually just a triangular shape which appears in the middle of the screen. The instructions consist of movements forwards and back, and turning through specified angles to the left and right. The turtle has a pen and can leave a trail, so that geometrical shapes may be drawn on the screen.

Even this very simple LOGO facility allows a lot of investigation of the geometry of shapes and angles; but it is the next step which brings in the power. Procedures can be written, adding new words to the vocabulary of the system. Different versions of LOGO vary a little, but the following is a typical definition of a triangle, with the length of side as a variable:

```
TO TRIANGLE : LENGTH
REPEAT 3 [FD : LENGTH RT 120]
END
```

The instruction TRIANGLE 250 will now produce on the screen an equilateral triangle with length of side 250 screen units.

Most LOGO work in schools is geometrical, and it has great potential in this respect. Recent extensions and developments allow the representation of three-dimensional objects in perspective, and a detailed study of geometrical loci. LOGO can also be used, however, to develop and explore microworlds other than the geometrical. Music, list processing and the construction of databases, and arithmetical activities are all possible environments.

Among the many articles on using LOGO in the classroom, Rahman (1988) describes an introduction for young children at a very basic level. Examples of geometrical procedures are provided by Leron (1988) and Fletcher (1989). Its use in other areas of mathematics is less well documented: one example of LOGO as a vehicle for exploring number is given by Gailiunas (1988).

In writing about the use of computers to provide microworlds for mathematics education, Bunyard (1989) raises a number of difficult issues. He expresses the belief that LOGO is the best example of a computer-based learning environment that is consistent with an individualistic interpretation of the aims of education. Certainly it can give pupils the opportunity to set their own tasks, create their own structures and identify relationships in their own way. Perhaps this should be the starting point for considering how new microworlds might be created and what might inspire them. Perhaps, too, it might be appropriate to consider how comparable environments can also be provided outside the context of microcomputers.

FACILITIES

Computers and calculators have various facilities which can provide alternative approaches to doing mathematics as well as to teaching and learning the subject. The National Curriculum indicates that we should recognise the existence of these facilities, and gear our teaching towards this recognition. Just as it has become ridiculous to ignore the widespread availability of calculators in our approach to arithmetic, so it is becoming necessary to take account of the facilities available in graphical work, in processing statistical data and in a growing number of other aspects of mathematical activity. The most obvious facilities for consideration in this context are graph-plotters, spreadsheets and information handling packages.

The algebra Attainment Target 7 of the National Curriculum requires that graphs are generated and interpreted on a calculator or computer. Graphical calculators are fairly common, and these can be an acceptable alternative to drawing graphs on paper in various situations. The difficulty of course is that the calculator does not provide a record of the graph for marking or assessment, and yet its graphic facility provides a useful means of investigating functions and solving equations.

A commonly used computer graph-plotting facility is FGP (ATM): Fowler (1988) describes a lesson in which this is used to investigate programs and compare the graphs of various equations and make generalisations about these. FGP is most often used in this way as a device to study algebraic functions; but it can also be used to fit graphs to experimental data. Williams (1989) describes some work in which FGP and MAKEFILE (ATM) are used in this way, to develop a mathematical model of a physical situation. Another type of graph-plotter Logoplotter (GEM) is described by Ball (1988) as a LOGO microworld concerned with plotting graphs. This facility offers a whole range of possibilities including statistical graphs, and gives the user a great deal of control over the way it operates.

Spreadsheets are mentioned in Attainment Target 5 where pupils at level 6 are required to 'use spreadsheets or other computer facilities to explore number patterns'. 'Other' computer facilities might well include NUMERATOR. On the other hand, spreadsheets are a useful facility in a variety of other contexts – for example in solving a range of polynomial equations by trial and improvement methods.

There are many articles describing ways of using spreadsheets in mathematics, and the Spring 1989 issue of *Micromath* makes a feature of these. In that journal, Straker provides a general survey of such usage. Hailwood explains the use of a spreadsheet in a geometrical problem while Ash-Mott and Rudolph describe its use in the solution of sets of linear equations. Articles by Byers and Megson give some ideas for spreadsheet work with younger children. Goodall (1988) shows how a spreadsheet can be used to enrich the work on optimisation, found in one chapter of the *SMP 11–16* books.

The information handling facility required by the National Curriculum was discussed earlier in Chapter 6. An adequate package for this is provided by MESU (1989), but more sophisticated database facilities in particular are sometimes useful. Again, the Autumn 1987 issue of *Micromath* includes a feature on this area. Wood gives an interesting introduction to this, in which he claims that computerised data-handling helps young people to work like real geographers, historians and scientists. This is very much a cross-curricular facility.

INTERACTIVE VIDEO

As well as improving the cleverness and sophistication of the settings and structures which computer software adopts in mathematics education, it is becoming important to improve the quality of visual display, of animation and of the sound upon which the material relies. Improvements in the technical quality of television monitors need to be matched by better recording and input techniques. The use of lasers provides a way forward in this. Laser audio-discs have brought higher standards of reproduction of sound through the use of compact disc players, and also allow fast random access without the sequential restraints of magnetic tape. In the same way, laser video-discs can give high quality sound and vision, access to any part of which can be controlled by computer.

At the time of writing the only commonly available material on video-disc is the Domesday project, which gives access to maps, photographs and information collected from many parts of Britain. Various devices associated with the material have applications in mathematics: the facilities for finding lengths and areas are obvious examples. Effectively, however, the project consists simply of a large database with easy access, but to which amendments and additions cannot be made. The laser disc allows the material to be presented in an attractive form, but the interaction is somewhat minimal.

It is difficult to know how interactive video might develop as a useful tool for learning mathematics. It is appealing to believe, like Kennett (1989), that the high quality images and sounds of laser technology will be able to create a new generation of mathematical microworlds. These would be attractive and sophisticated environments in which structures could be created and ideas explored. If interactive video really can develop in this way, and be commercially and economically viable, then it will surely have effects reaching far beyond its applications in mathematics education.

Chapter 12

Examinations and assessment

ASSESSMENT IN SCHOOL MATHEMATICS

A lot of the resources which are put into mathematics education are expended on assessment. Teachers spend a lot of their time checking and marking pupils' work and keeping records of pupils' performance. Regular assessment at the end of each key stage is seen as the mechanism by which the National Curriculum will be enforced; and it is into this aspect of the work that much of the money will go – paid out to the consortia who have contracted to organise various parts of the testing. To set GCSE and, for that matter, A-level examinations, there are examination boards and groups with large budgets, staff and property, constituting a major service industry.

It is perhaps surprising that all this is taken so much for granted. It could after all be argued that British education is concerned obsessively with assessment. Pirie (1989) describes it as a sad, but nonetheless true, indictment of British educational society that 'if it is not seen to be assessed, it is not seen to be valued'. A large proportion of educational time, money and effort is allocated not to providing effective teaching and learning but to checking up on what has been taught and learned. As the assessment demands of the National Curriculum have become clear, some observers have commented that, however often children are measured, this does not make them grow any more quickly. Yet, despite such occasional expressions of cynicism, the assessment monster has generally been allowed to grow, with hardly a murmur of disapproval.

Political rhetoric often appears to be based on the belief that testing is a means of raising standards. A contrasting and worrying expectation is that it can trivialise and stultify work in schools. Denvir (1988) considers that, in response to imposed assessment, teachers will prepare children to perform well. In many cases this preparation will mean the rehearsal of pupils' responses to improve their scores. This process seeks, quite deliberately, to cover up lack of understanding of ideas, and to discourage imaginative behaviour.

FORMS AND FUNCTIONS OF ASSESSMENT

There are many ways in which the processes of assessment can be studied and subdivided. In the previous section, this was done in a superficial way, according to the *context* of the assessment. Thus three distinct areas were identified: marking of pupils' work on a regular basis, the key stage assessment requirements of the National Curriculum, and the GCSE and A-level examination system.

Sometimes the terms *formative* and *summative* assessment are used. Essentially, formative assessment is made with the assumption that further teaching and learning will take the results into account: it looks forward to the pupils' learning needs. Summative assessment is concerned with identifying what has been achieved: it implies a judgment on the outcome of previous learning. Of course, in a particular situation, the distinction may be blurred; but, if the purpose of some test or other assessment procedure is questioned, it can be useful to try to express it in these terms. Sometimes, it seems that tests are just a part of classroom routine with no clear rationale.

Pirie (1989), who is particularly concerned with classroom-based assessment, produces a classification by asking who is supposed to benefit from it. From this point of view, reasons for assessing fall into three categories: for the benefit of the pupil, for the benefit of the teacher, and to satisfy the perceived needs of others. Marking pupils' work, for example, can be justified in these terms. It provides pupils with feedback on how correct or worthwhile their work is. It keeps the teacher informed about pupils' progress and the success or otherwise of the teaching and learning which is taking place. The sight of marked work lets parents, colleagues and any other interested parties know that the teacher is a conscientious, caring person who takes a proper, professional interest in the pupils.

Denvir (1988) provides a categorisation of the purposes of assessment, identifying assessment for teaching, for selection, for evaluation and for curriculum control. Again the categories can sometimes be blurred, and it is not claimed that these cover all intentions. Some form of assessment may also be introduced, for example, to motivate pupils or teachers, or to report to parents. It is clear too that the idea of 'purpose' admits of various nuances. It might refer to the reason for the existence of a particular assessment procedure, which may be largely historical; or to the motivation for introducing it, which has political implications; or to its effective function – its influence on pupils, teachers and the curriculum.

From the present point of view, the historical and political perspectives are interesting but largely beyond our control. Assessment structures are in place, and it is how they actually operate and affect schools, teachers and pupils which is important. Interpreted in this way, the categories focus on the function of assessment in terms of:

- its influence on classroom decisions, made on a day-to-day basis by teachers and pupils;
- its influence on decisions taken by individual pupils (or, sadly, taken by others for them) about their lives and future activities;

- its use in evaluating the curriculum, comparing schools, appraising teachers, and generally making judgments about the whole system;
- its use as a mechanism for curriculum control.

MARKING

It is a commonly held view that school mathematics generates a great deal of marking, and indeed the Cockcroft Report (1982) made specific reference to this. For this reason, marking looms large amongst the tasks required of mathematics teachers: marking and preparation are the activities most usually quoted as occupying teachers' attention outside school hours. With these considerations in mind, commercially produced schemes and textbooks have often provided 'teachers' books', containing lists of answers, which might be seen as reducing the burden of marking.

In reality, however, marking which can be reduced to a simple mechanical exercise is hardly a valuable use of a hard-pressed teacher's time, and is not likely to prove particularly informative to pupils. Ticks and crosses in themselves are of little assistance. Indeed, the results of exercises involving routine practice or applications, which have definite 'right' answers, are often most sensibly checked by the pupils themselves. Such an approach is arguably valuable as one way in which pupils can take greater responsibility for their own work and progress. Cockcroft also suggested that pupils might check the results of computational exercises with a calculator. This is of course possible for exercises in pencil-and-paper arithmetic; but, if pupils can be so much more sure of obtaining accurate answers with a calculator, it might well be questioned whether the pencil-and-paper approach has any real value.

In many problems, the real difficulty is in deciding what calculation is appropriate rather than performing the computational arithmetic; and in such cases calculator checks may not be especially relevant.

It is pointed out in another chapter that the statements of attainment in the National Curriculum which demand arithmetical calculations without the use of a calculator can be turned into a more open-ended, investigational activity. Pupils might be asked whether they know, or can find or can devise a method for multiplying a three-digit number by a two-digit number, for example. In such an exercise, the validity of the suggested method can be confirmed by means of a calculator. The teacher's role in marking pupils' work then becomes not so much a matter of checking whether answers are right or wrong but of evaluating the pupils' activities.

The last remark leads into the issues involved in marking investigations, projects and individual coursework. While such marking may require some correction of errors, this is not the main concern. The nature and format of the work may be determined by pupils rather than prescribed by the teacher. Assessment may involve consideration not just of whether the work is correct, but of how ambitious the tasks are which pupils attempt, the level of sophistication of the approach, and an overall evaluation of how worthwhile the activity is.

In GCSE examinations, coursework has to be assessed in as objective a manner as a written examination. One of the concerns of the examining boards has been to provide well-defined criteria on which to base this assessment. Outside the framework of formal assessment procedures, however, teachers' evaluation of projects or investigation work is tempered by their knowledge of pupils' abilities. Inevitably, marking has to reflect this. The demands made on pupils, and the acceptability of the response to these demands, will not be the same for everyone.

Whether work in mathematics is routine or whether it involves pupils in more open, creative activity, teachers need to use marking to maintain a general overview of pupil progress. Regular marking has diagnostic and supportive functions. It enables the teacher to become aware of mistakes and misunderstandings which arise, and encourages pupils to seek help when necessary. Good marking can make both the diagnosis of the mistake and the encouragement to seek help clear and explicit: simply marking a question wrong usually serves neither purpose.

There is enormous variation in the style of marking adopted by teachers and in the time and care which they devote to this. There are basic minimum requirements, however. It cannot be satisfactory, for example, if pupils continue to repeat a particular mistake because some idea or method has not been understood: marking must at least enable this to be picked up and corrected. Correction in this sense may involve a class lesson on a particular topic, or additional help for individual pupils.

Cockcroft identified some situations in which it was felt that pupils were not being set enough work because teachers were unable to find the time to mark it. Marking has to be a response to pupils' work, not a restraint upon it. If detailed marking is given such a priority that it determines how much work is done, something is wrong. Perhaps it means that the teacher's pattern of working needs to change. Most probably it means that the amount of independence and responsibility which pupils are given for their own work in mathematics could well be increased.

KEEPING RECORDS

All teachers acquire a great deal of knowledge about their pupils. Decisions have always been made in schools about what written records should be kept, and how these records can be concise and accurate. The National Curriculum requirements, however, create more specific demands; and teachers were advised by Circular 17/89 that their records are now needed to serve the following purposes:

- to record the attainment targets and statements of attainment which each pupil has attempted;
- to show the achievement level which each pupil has reached;

- to give an indication of the progress of each individual pupil in relation to attainment targets and statements of attainment;
- to provide evidence to support the levels of attainment reached;
- to give parents and other teachers and schools access to information about their children's academic achievement, other skills and abilities, and progress in school.

The last point is particularly reminiscent of the argument in the Cockcroft Report that a record of a pupil's progress is needed not only as a reminder to the teacher and for the information of the head or head of department, but also to enable continuity to be maintained when the pupil changes teacher or school.

Many published schemes for secondary mathematics, especially those providing for an individualised approach, incorporate a detailed system of record keeping. Where a more didactic style of class teaching is adopted, some teachers have been accustomed to keeping records of work set in class or for homework, and of pupils' performance on this work, in a mark book. Sometimes, such record-keeping has been the responsibility of the mathematics department; often, it has to a large extent been left as a matter for the individual teacher responsible for a particular class. The National Curriculum has created the need for closer co-operation amongst all teachers in this matter: it means that whole-school policies on recording and record-keeping are now being developed.

The School Examinations and Assessment Council (SEAC) has produced a guide to teacher assessment (1990) which offers some general guidance on recording in the context of the National Curriculum at Key Stages 1 and 2. At the time of writing, it remains to be seen whether more detailed guidance will be provided for teachers in secondary schools; but it is certainly the view of some teachers that the advice offered by SEAC on these matters so far has been patronising and not particularly helpful. Several issues, however, are emerging as important:

- Records must be closely related to what happens in the classroom. They need to be easy to complete in that context, so that they do not interfere with or interrupt teaching and learning.
- Care needs to be taken that information recorded is useful and relevant. Records are valuable if they can be used to make decisions about pupils' work in the future.
- Records need to be easily comprehensible to people who have not been involved in compiling them. They will be used for communicating and reporting.
- Records should be useful to pupils too. However the information is made available, pupils need to be involved in an informed way in their own learning and assessment.

ASSESSMENT AND CLASSROOM DECISIONS

Checking and marking pupils' work, setting tests in the classroom and keeping records of pupils' achievement have genuine value if these form a basis for decisions about classroom activities. At an obvious level, a teacher working on a topic with the whole class, who discovers that most of the pupils are coping easily and successfully with the work (or, in contrast, that most are not coping at all), will make revised decisions about what to do next on the basis of this information. Also, if individual pupils are out of step with most of the class, because they have little understanding, or because their understanding is way ahead, or because they have a strikingly different perception of or approach to the work, then effective assessment will highlight this. The responsibility of the teacher is then presumably to provide suitable alternative, remedial or enrichment material.

In individualised learning systems, the mechanisms of marking, testing and record-keeping are an essential part of the scheme. Again, on this basis, decisions about pupils' next activity are normally the responsibility of the teacher, although more responsive practice might allow this to be a matter for negotiation between teacher and pupil. In situations where independent learning is being promoted genuinely, pupils may have a large say in what work they do, with guidance from the teacher and on the basis of assessment with appropriate feedback.

Decisions about classroom activity may involve not only the content and level of the work but also the organisation of lessons. Whole class teaching, small-group work or individualised work might be interrupted or modified to take account of pupils' responses. If judgment about these matters is to be based on assessment rather than the whim of the teacher, then that assessment is likely to need to address affective issues such as motivation and attitude as well as pupils' cognitive performance. Good classroom assessment involves monitoring a range of learning outcomes, even if these are inevitably sometimes judged in more subjective and less formal ways.

It is perhaps worth questioning the use of class tests in mathematics lessons. The test papers which some individualised schemes provide are useful ways of reviewing the progress of individual pupils to determine how they should proceed; and whole class tests can have a similar value – they give the teacher an indication of how much has been learned and what different needs particular pupils have. Unfortunately, a class test is often presented as a motivating device – a stick or carrot to encourage pupils to work and revise. In many schools, teachers and pupils alike are accustomed to thinking of tests in this way. It is a well-established feature of mathematics teaching, which has a certain effectiveness because it is accepted, and which will no doubt continue. From an idealistic viewpoint, however, it is recognisably unsatisfactory. The motivation for learning is entirely extrinsic to any interest or perceived value in the mathematical activity. At its worst, this motivation may rely on the public praise or shame which the test scores convey, creating a competitive exercise of a somewhat unsavoury kind.

EXAMINATIONS AT 16+

Often, an assessment procedure is used to enable pupils to make decisions about what they can and should do next. These decisions might involve further study, or employment, or plans to take up or not to take up particular interests in life. Often, too, the result of the assessment takes away some of the options – selection procedures for various courses and jobs will preclude those without certain qualifications.

One of the focal points of British society's demand for qualifications is performance in mathematics at 16+. Your grade in mathematics at GCSE or its equivalent is a significant factor in determining whether you go on to take A-levels, what A-levels you choose, what further education courses you will consider and what kind of job you will apply for. The work you have done in mathematics – and especially the difference between a C grade and a D or an E at GCSE – may not be of any great relevance or significance; but, so long as most people believe it is, and especially so long as pupils and students themselves believe it is, then its importance as a 'ticket' will be maintained.

Of course, this is an overstatement. Of course, there will be plenty of opportunities later. Of course, people with no qualifications in mathematics lead satisfying and successful lives. Nevertheless, the pressure is there. Doing well in mathematics at school is considered important; and the implication of this is that we value more highly those lifestyles and careers to which a higher grade in the subject is likely to lead. This external pressure provides some motivation, but can also be a source of frustration. Inevitably, it gives teachers of mathematics a certain amount of leverage, and some may choose to remind pupils of the significance of the subject in these terms. Emphasising this, however, is hardly appropriate; and, for the majority of pupils who are not going to achieve a high grade in mathematics, such emphasis could be described as cruel.

When the school-leaving age was raised to 16 in the 1970s, the demand for a school-leaving examination rose sharply and many more pupils were entered for CSE examinations. In spite of the efforts of teachers to produce examinations of a fresh and appropriate style at this level, CSE continued to be seen as a second-rate, watered down version of O-level. The intention to develop a common examination system at 16+ was announced in the early 1980s, and 'National Criteria' on which all such GCSE examinations must be based were published in 1985. In 1988, for the first time, all pupils in the relevant year of schooling who sat an examination were entered for GCSE.

GCSE grades are awarded on a single seven-point scale, A, B, C, D, E, F and G. In mathematics, all GCSE examinations are limited-grade: that is a candidate is entered at a particular level and only certain grades can be achieved. For GCSE purposes, the large number of boards previously setting O-level and CSE examinations were organised into five groups (in England and Wales) on a regional basis. These groups have adopted slightly different arrangements and nomenclature; but, in mathematics at least, all allow pupils to be entered at three different levels called variously 1, 2 and 3, or P, Q and R, or foundation, intermediate and higher. Commonly, grades E, F and G are available at foundation level; C, D, E and F at intermediate level; and A, B, C and D at higher level. All allow for some overlap, but a pupil entered at higher level, for example, who does not achieve the marks required for grade D at that level will not receive a grade at all.

The arrangements for setting examination papers at different levels vary as well. In some cases there may be quite separate papers for each level. Other groups have adopted a four-in-line model, in which papers 1 and 2 are taken at foundation level, 2 and 3 at intermediate level, and 3 and 4 at higher level.

As well as examination papers, all GCSE examining groups must provide a coursework element. From 1988 to 1990 this has been optional, but from 1991 coursework must form part of the assessment for all pupils. Some groups of schools have made arrangements with examining groups to develop GCSE assessment procedures based entirely on coursework. Assessment by coursework alone is less common in mathematics, however, than in some other subjects.

In 1994 some reconciliation is required between the GCSE and the assessment requirements of the National Curriculum, as the phased introduction of the latter reaches the end of Key Stage 4 in mathematics. The National Curriculum requires all assessment to be partly based on standard tests and partly teacher controlled. This will fit the broad pattern of GCSE mathematics, but it seems likely to put an end to assessment schemes based on coursework alone.

GCSE grades A–G need to be translated into levels of the National Curriculum. It is suggested that the attainment required by a GCSE grade A is National Curriculum level 9, and thus grade A will be replaced by two levels. Level 10 is more advanced than the previous minimum demands of any GCSE grade. Levels and grades do not correspond neatly, but the lowest GCSE grade G is likely to represent level 4. The description of attainment at 16+ in terms of levels, with higher numbers representing higher achievement, is in a sense more satisfactory than the GCSE grading system. It has proved difficult for pupils, parents and employers to accept grades F and G, for example, as representing any kind of positive achievement: they are more likely to be regarded as fail grades.

The intention in developing GCSE was to move towards a system which is criterion-referenced rather than norm-referenced. There is no predetermined, theoretical distribution of results across the seven grades: rather, a particular grade represents a defined level of achievement. The levels of the National Curriculum are of course criterion-referenced in detail by the statements of attainment. This feature of the assessment system means that any overall rise or fall in standards should be identifiable as a shift in the distribution of grades or levels achieved. On the whole, the results of the second cohort of GCSE examinations in 1989 were better than the first round in 1988. It is debatable, however, whether this represented a real increase in pupils' competence or was simply a reflection of teachers' increased appreciation of the demands of the examination and consequent ability to prepare their pupils more directly for this.

ASSESSMENT, EVALUATION AND THE NATIONAL CURRICULUM

As explained in Chapter 1, at or near the end of each key stage the achievement of each individual pupil must be assessed in each of the relevant attainment targets. Assessment is by a combination of externally determined standard assessment tasks (SATs) and teachers' own assessments. The basis for these arrangements was formulated by the Task Group on Assessment and Testing (TGAT). The Schools Examination and Assessment Council (SEAC) continues to consider and advise on the detailed development and implementation of these arrangements.

The recorded assessments of individual pupils have to be made available to parents and other interested parties, and the recorded aggregate results of schools must be made available for more general publication. It is clearly intended that this information can be used not only as a record of the progress of individual pupils but as a means of evaluating schools and appraising the standard of teaching. Circular 6/89 (DES/HMSO) states:

> The level reached by a pupil at any given age will reflect the number of years of schooling he or she has had, what they have been taught and how well, and individual ability and maturity.

Some indication of how results might be published is provided by an earlier DES document (1989):

> Schools *will* be *required* to publish the unadjusted results of pupils in aggregate, at ages 11, 14 and 16.
>
> In publishing data on results schools may set them out against relevant background information.

Also, strangely, the document tells local education authorities (LEAs) what they do not have to do:

> LEAs will *not* be *required* to publish 'league tables' for the schools in their area.

LEAs are not prevented from doing this, however; and, if they do not do so, the press will no doubt be willing to do it for them. Experience of media handling of published performance data on universities, for example, suggests that newspapers will not be afraid to draw up league tables. Furthermore, the information may not always be presented in the most sensitive and helpful way.

It is to be hoped that the assessment procedures will be used not only to evaluate the performance of pupils and schools, but also to review the appropriateness of the specified attainment targets. All the details can be changed by the Secretary of State in the light of advice from the National Curriculum Council.

CURRICULUM CONTROL

The assessment arrangements are a mechanism by which the implementation of the National Curriculum can be enforced. In mathematics the curriculum is defined by the attainment targets, which were set specifically to establish what children should normally be expected to know, understand and be able to do at the ages of 7, 11, 14 and 16, and to enable the progress of each child to be measured against national standards. In this sense, the National Curriculum is assessment-led. The objectives to be assessed are spelled out, and these control what happens in the classroom.

Any external imposed assessment procedure acts as a controlling influence on the curriculum. Thus for some teachers, anxious to promote investigations and more open-ended work in mathematics, the development of a GCSE coursework element has appeared as an adaptation of the examination system to the changing curriculum. For many teachers, however, the opposite process has happened; and it is changes in the method of assessment which have pushed through the curriculum changes. For most people, GCSE coursework represents an assessment-led curriculum change.

For quite a number of years now, schools or groups of schools involved in innovative curriculum development projects have been able to make their own assessment arrangements at 16+ in co-operation with the examination boards. This has allowed imaginative work to grow without the tight restraint of an imposed assessment structure. Section 16 of the Education Reform Act appears to allow for similar replacement or modification of the National Curriculum requirements, to enable experimental curriculum development to flourish. It will be interesting to see whether and to what extent schools will be able to take advantage of this. It may well prove difficult politically; and, in the early years at least, such disapplication of the National Curriculum is likely to be rare. The way is left open for innovation, however, and it is to be hoped that enthusiastic teachers will feel able to make proposals of this kind.

Despite the view that their inclusion in GCSE assessment gives project work and investigations a respectable legitimacy, there are those who feel that this immediately weakens and devalues them. Lerman (1989) sees the danger as a loss of what open-endedness exists in school mathematics to examination-led criteria for assessment of children's work. This unease is provoked merely by GCSE, with its commitment to coursework: in this respect, the National Curriculum is even more disquieting. Lerman even goes so far as to suggest that we should perhaps forget assessment for some years, until we have developed new ways of working in the classroom, and give every child a 'pass' in the meantime. It is a forlorn dream.

Chapter 13

Attitudes to mathematics

INTRODUCTION

Through their experiences in school mathematics, children learn (or sometimes fail to learn) knowledge, skills and ideas as a result of the work they do. At the same time, they develop attitudes towards the subject. The teaching, the discussion, the activities developed and indeed the entire curriculum convey messages, whether deliberately or not, about mathematics, which influence these attitudes. To most teachers this is a source of some concern: most feel it important that favourable attitudes to the subject are created and fostered. This view is justified in a variety of ways.

There is a common and reasonable belief that positive attitudes, particularly liking for, and interest in, mathematics, lead to greater effort and in turn to higher achievement. While there is evidence to support this assumption, the link between attitudes and achievement is not so close as might be expected; and there are obviously other variables which affect both attitude and achievement. What is more clear is the strong relationship between attitude and the choice of mathematics for further study: pupils who claim to enjoy the subject are more likely to choose mathematics courses in the sixth form or in higher education.

Positive attitudes, however, can be regarded as valid objectives of mathematics education in their own right. Affective learning outcomes – such as enjoyment, enthusiasm, fascination, appreciation – may be taken into account alongside the more cognitive aspects of learning mathematics which are measured in terms of achievement. In the evaluation of the activities of teaching and learning, all these features are part of children's mathematical performance.

It is also possible to see, in pupils' affective response to mathematical activity, the roots of personal qualities and characteristics which may persist into adult life. Desirable qualities, which most people would want to encourage, include confidence, independence, imagination, co-operation, flexibility and persistence. Less constructively, school mathematics seems to have the potential to engender unhelpful characteristics such as anxiety, helplessness and apathy.

CANVASSING CHILDREN'S OPINIONS OF MATHEMATICS

There are several possible approaches to determining children's attitudes; and the choice depends rather on what it is intended to measure. One approach is to canvas opinion by means of a structured questionnaire, which may commonly consist of a list of statements with which children are asked to agree or disagree. Examples might be the following.

- Usually I enjoy mathematics.
- You will not get very far in life if you can't do maths.
- Mathematics is a difficult subject.

A scale of alternative responses may be provided, such as strongly agree, agree, don't know, disagree, strongly disagree. These examples illustrate the different dimensions in which attitudes have usually been analysed: like/dislike, useful/not useful and easy/hard.

Various studies of this nature were carried out in the 1960s and 1970s. Some of them compared attitudes to a number of subjects, so that mathematics appeared in a kind of league table, according to one or more criteria. The culmination of this style of research, however, is to be found in the six APU primary and secondary surveys published in 1980–2. These surveys include extensive information about children's attitudes, both to mathematics as a whole and to different topics within mathematics, in terms of the sort of dimensions already described.

In comparisons between subjects, mathematics usually occupies a low position on the liking scale, although a large proportion of pupils are identified as believing mathematics to be useful. The APU surveys provide a great deal of material which is not easily summarised. Amongst 11-year-old children, faith in the usefulness of mathematics is well established, but other aspects of attitudes towards mathematics are less consistent. The most accurate answer to the question of whether primary school children enjoy mathematics is 'sometimes': liking and difficulty are not so much associated with the whole subject as with specific activities, topics and forms of presentation which occur in mathematics lessons. These surveys were carried out in the late 1970s, so that they reflect the style and emphasis predominant in primary schools at that time. In the 'number' category, for example, arithmetical computations are the most popular, receiving more liking responses than any other topic. Next come questions about fractions, decimals and percentages; while those concerned with concepts and structures, such as factors and prime numbers, are least liked.

Overall, there is little identifiable difference in attitude between boys and girls at this stage, although some differences show up in their responses to different topics. The questionnaire used allowed a response 'uncertain', and in general girls are more inclined to choose this than boys are: this is especially striking in the 'measures' (length, area, volume, money, weight and time) category.

During the secondary years, self-reported attitudes to mathematics deteriorate amongst all groups of pupils. There is, in fact, quite a lot of evidence of age-related decline in attitudes to all school subjects. As children grow older they tend to report less favourable (or more critical) reactions to a variety of experiences, and this change could be considered as part of the maturing process. Attitudes to mathematics, however, decline in a differentiated way. The acceptance that mathematics is useful, although weakened in secondary schools, stands up relatively well, whereas pupils become much more likely to dislike mathematics and to describe it as hard. In all these dimensions, the deterioration is more pronounced amongst girls than amongst boys.

The link between attitudes and gender differences is a subtle one. There is a common and plausible belief that the disadvantaged position of girls in mathematics is to a large extent the result of sex role stereotyping – that girls are conditioned to the opinion that mathematics is a boys' subject. In one of the APU secondary surveys, this issue is addressed directly, with questions which ask pupils what differences there are between boys and girls in learning mathematics. The results show a surprising inconsistency, with roughly equal numbers believing that boys or girls are at an advantage, and many pupils are convinced that there is no difference. This apparent anomaly and a more detailed explanation and interpretation of the findings are explored in Chapter 15.

Children's opinions as described in this section do of course derive from a variety of sources, from parents, teachers, the media and the general ethos of society, as well as from the children's own classroom experience. Opinions are easily hardened and rationalised: they become a standpoint rather than a personal, affective reaction, and they certainly are not always reflected in children's apparent responses in mathematics lessons.

Another issue is the labelling of a particular opinion as favourable or positive. In the easy hard dimension, for example, agreement with statements describing mathematics as easy is normally taken to indicate confidence and a positive attitude of personal capability. There are some mathematically very able people, however, who regard mathematics as a very hard subject, at which only clever people can succeed: this is obviously a very positive attitude for the purpose of self-esteem. Similarly the favourableness of the useful/not useful scale depends on the value which the individual attaches to practical usefulness in judging whether an activity is worthwhile: it is part of a personal philosophy of life. Amongst sixth-form students, belief in the usefulness of mathematics is characteristic of a bias towards science and technology rather than indicative of motivation towards further study in mathematics.

Finally, these statements of opinion, by their very nature, begin as adult views of what children's attitudes to mathematics might be. Pupils presented with such statements may not otherwise have thought in such terms at all; and the statements themselves may plant ideas in their minds. The opinions elicited are no doubt honest, but they may be somewhat peripheral to the real, emotional response of children towards mathematical activity.

PERCEPTIONS OF THE NATURE OF MATHEMATICS

Another aspect of the study of attitudes is the attempt to determine the overall perception which individuals have of the nature of mathematics – what kind of subject or activity it is. Some such perceptions are as follows:

(a) Mathematics is a set of facts and standard rules which need to be learned, often by rote, and remembered. Correct methods and procedures and ways of setting things out are all important, as is precision in the use of language and symbolism.

(b) Mathematics is a way of better understanding the real world: it provides frameworks and models to describe reality, and enables us to solve problems in these real situations.

(c) Mathematics is about recognising and classifying structures and patterns and relationships.

(d) Mathematics is a creative, problem-solving activity. The pleasure and entertainment it provides are those of solving puzzles, and of logical thinking.

(e) (from the Cockcroft Report) Mathematics provides a means of communication which is powerful, concise and unambiguous.

(f) (from the National Curriculum proposals) In the broadest sense, mathematics provides a means for organising, communicating and manipulating information.

(g) (from *Better Mathematics*) Thus, for children, mathematics should be a kind of learning which requires a minimum of factual knowledge and a great deal of experience in dealing with situations using particular kinds of thinking skills.

(h) Mathematics is the ability to use calculators, microcomputers and other technological aids to calculation sensibly.

(i) Mathematics is being able to do calculations without needing a calculator.

The varied ideas which people have about what mathematics is, whether pupils, teachers, parents, politicians or industrialists, are so disparate that it can be difficult to realise that they are talking about the same activity. This is illustrated in some detail by the material in the report *Better Mathematics* (1987), especially in Chapter 2, 'Children Learning Mathematics'. The chapter includes the statement:

> Most difficulties in mathematics teaching hinge on the perception by pupils, teachers and parents of the nature and purpose of the mathematics in which they are engaged.

It seems likely that most people's perceptions of mathematics are formed by their own experience of learning the subject at school. This means that many regard the subject as a collection of established knowledge and procedures – calculations, proofs and standard methods. Either it is seen very much as a school subject – and a somewhat arduous one – or it is a set of utilitarian skills which are needed for adult life and work. Relatively rarely is it suggested as an activity which is interesting and worthwhile in itself. Many people have an interest in literature, music, art or craft which they pursue for intrinsic satisfaction as a leisure activity: few are able to look upon mathematics in this way.

Mathematics teachers may be seen as just that: indeed in some ways the mathematics teacher is the archetypal teacher, and certainly not a practitioner in the way that teachers of art, music or PE may well be. Such teachers may be artists, musicians or sports people in their own right, but mathematics teachers are rather less likely to be involved in doing mathematics at their own level, experiencing the kinds of difficulties and excitement which their classes should also be feeling. If teachers maintain, discover or rediscover enthusiasm for and personal engagement in mathematical activity for themselves, then they are more likely to convey enhanced perceptions of the nature of mathematics to their pupils.

Another common perception about mathematics is that it is closely associated with failure, and that being bad at mathematics is quite acceptable. The notion that successful, educated people need not be embarrassed but can be rather proud of their inadequate mathematical ability is absurd and patently counter-productive. It is a caricature which needs to be discredited.

The utilitarian value of mathematics is one of its most recognised attributes. It is surely this perception which has given the subject its unquestioned, compulsory status, although, at its most debased level, the perception is reduced to the recognition that some kind of qualification in the subject is an essential ticket to many careers or courses of higher education. One consequence of the utilitarian principle is the search for relevance. Yet this is often unhelpful, particularly when it implies relevance to some hypothetical future style of adult life: few people, for example, would find checking gas and electricity accounts motivating. The important criterion is that the activity should be recognised as worthwhile for the pupils or students; and this may mean that it should make sense in terms of their lives and interests as they genuinely are, and not as teachers, employers or politicians might wish or pretend or imagine they are. This aspect of relevance is considered in more detail in the context of pupils' cultural and ethnic backgrounds in Chapter 16.

The essential conclusion of this section is that it would be helpful to promote broader, more eclectic perceptions about the nature of mathematics. Many people have a narrowly restricted view of what mathematics is, and, if that restricted picture is unattractive to them, then they dislike mathematics. Yet mathematics encompasses an enormous range and variety of activity and different people may be involved in totally different activities while still claiming, justifiably, to be doing mathematics. To use a slightly irreverent analogy, it is a very broad church. If we compare it with music, for example, most people can find some music which they can listen to, or dance to, or sing, or play, or enjoy in some way. Mathematics has at least as wide a scope.

CHILDREN'S EMOTIONAL RESPONSE TO MATHEMATICS

It has already been mentioned that canvassing children's opinions in the way described earlier does not necessarily identify the focus and intensity of their affective response to mathematical activity in the classroom – indeed, it is not necessarily intended for this purpose.

Attempts can be made to discover the nature of pupils' emotional responses, either by observing and interpreting their immediate behaviour in the classroom, or by asking them to recall, describe and reflect upon events or situations which had a particular significance for them. This description of remembered experiences can provide pupils with a more articulate and meaningful way of expressing their feelings than can any collection of opinions or generalities.

A discussion of these considerations and a description of her own approach to such investigation has been provided by Celia Hoyles (1982), who interviewed 14-year-old pupils, asking them to tell stories about times during which they had felt particularly good or particularly bad when learning. The research also aimed to discover how frequently stories about mathematics might be told and to identify the features of these mathematics stories. Out of 281 stories collected, 114 (about 40 per cent) were concerned with mathematics – considerably in excess of the proportion of time given to the subject in the school curriculum. Of these 114, 72 (over 63 per cent) were bad while in all the other areas taken together the proportion of bad stories was less than half.

In these stories, the actual mathematical content of the work was rarely mentioned, while in other areas vivid descriptions of the activity were often included. Not only did the pupils not describe the mathematics, they also tended not to comment on its interest, relevance or future use.

Research of this nature demonstrates conflicts of expectations amongst pupils, as well as pupil expectations which seem at variance with good educational practice. For example, many pupils want security and structure in mathematics lessons and expect teachers to 'make it easy' or 'explain how to do it': this is perceived as a way in which tension and anxiety could be relieved. Such an approach, however, could discourage investigation and creativity and would inhibit pupils from taking any responsibility for their own work. Many pupils are concerned simply with the outcome of their work – doing it, finishing it, getting it right; and this concern appears to distract them from any involvement in the subject itself. Pupils appear to want grades and assessment as an indication of their mathematical ability and they judge themselves highly if they do well, yet find it difficult to rationalise any failure.

Thomas and Costello (1988) adopted a comparable, though somewhat naive approach, and asked 11- and 14-year-old pupils to write about times when they felt good and bad in mathematics lessons and to describe just how they felt. The responses show a considerable degree of consistency, and allow a number of generalisations to be made about the ways in which pupils react in mathematics lessons. Again, it is notable that pupils almost never mention the subject matter of the lesson and, when they do, it is as a reference point for the time and occasion ('it was when we were doing ...') rather than the focus of the pupils' emotional response.

It appears usual for pupils to attribute good experience in mathematics to their own prowess but bad experience is less easily handled. Often it is blamed on the inadequacy of the teacher – this is hardly surprising, and is a good defence mechanism. Although the rationalisation may differ, both types of experience tend to be interpreted in a highly personalised way. It is not the mathematical activity but the personal status of self and classmates and teacher which is the focus of attention.

There are some gender differences in affective responses: most notable is the greater tendency of girls to expect failure and to be surprised by success. Ironically this is more often apparent in experiences described as good, for example, '... I felt very happy and joyful because *for once* I felt as if I could do something right ...'.

In the light of these discussions, it is worth suggesting two aspects of life in the mathematics classroom which merit careful consideration. One is the way in which teachers react and respond to pupils' performance; and the second is the role of the teacher as a focus of attention.

Praising and blaming children and offering reward and punishment are part of the mathematics teacher's stock-in-trade. These are reflected in children's attitudinal responses, whether in terms of their self-image or their view of the teacher. Strategies which improve pupils' self-esteem may be preferable to those which damage the pupil–teacher relationship, but all these things have the sad effect of distracting attention from the mathematical activity. Extrinsic objectives become more important than learning.

Perhaps this is unavoidable. We all tend to personalise responses: some of us are very good at telling other people that they are wonderful or brilliant or stupid. We rarely mean it. Sometimes it might be better simply to say how interesting and exciting this experience which we have shared has been, or to say that this activity has not worked out very well, and share our disappointment. In either case we can look for ways of creating good experience in the future. These ideas seem to have a particular relevance to teaching and learning mathematics.

For the teacher to adopt a strong performing role in the classroom and to orchestrate the class in a way which puts the spotlight on individual pupils can sometimes generate unhelpful emotional responses which have no bearing on learning mathematics. In the consideration of mixed-ability teaching and individualised learning in Chapter 10, the discussion of classroom organisation and the role of the teacher centred mainly on catering effectively for the broad spread of ability. Arguments for particular organisational systems are commonly made in this way, on essentially cognitive grounds. Yet some of the tension and anxiety of mathematics lessons can be softened in schools where individualised learning is the norm. At least, this might be one consideration in developing a mathematics scheme and setting out the teacher's role in it.

SUMMARY

Pupils' attitudes to mathematics merit concern for a number of reasons: they may affect achievement and participation in mathematics courses at a later stage; they may form the roots of personal qualities which persist into adult life and may be considered either beneficial or undesirable; and affective learning outcomes – such as enjoyment, enthusiasm, fascination, appreciation – may be counted as worthwhile objectives in themselves.

A lot of traditional research on attitudes canvasses children's opinions in structured questionnaires which require children to agree or disagree with statements. The APU surveys, in particular, provide a great deal of information about these matters. Such opinions may become hardened and rationalised standpoints, but they are not necessarily incorporated into pupils' behaviour and emotional responses in the classroom.

A major concern is the perception which everyone has – pupils, teachers, parents, politicians, employers – of the nature of mathematics. Such perceptions are variable and individualistic, but are usually narrow and restricted. The promotion of a broader view of what constitutes mathematical activity could serve to broaden the appeal of the subject.

Finally, the emotional response of pupils to mathematics lessons is often intense, often concerned with the pupils' self-esteem or the status and adequacy of the teacher, and rarely concerned with the mathematical activity and subject matter of the lesson. Affective issues of this kind could be taken into consideration in discussing ways in which teachers interact with pupils, forms of classroom organisation, and the teacher's role in providing mathematical activity.

Chapter 14

Individual differences and special needs

SPECIAL NEEDS IN LEARNING MATHEMATICS

Most books and a lot of the research on mathematical education are concerned with explaining the ways in which most pupils are alike in learning mathematics. This is not unreasonable. It is useful to make good generalisations about learning in order to determine what kind of teaching and classroom activity is likely to prove effective. Idiosyncratic behaviour on the part of individual children may be interesting but it may not provide any widely applicable insight.

On the other hand, the broad spread of ability in mathematics is increasingly well recognised. It is accepted that pupils differ considerably both in their potential for learning mathematics and in their actual achievement. The 7 year gap, referred to by Cockcroft and quoted in Chapter 1, is a public acknowledgment of this variation. Yet even this idea reflects a belief in a consistent pattern of learning. It suggests that there is a notional progression in mathematics along which all pupils develop, even though pupils of the same age may be at quite different stages and may develop at different rates.

At the same time, it is common for teachers, parents and others to believe that many children do not come anywhere near achieving their maximum potential in mathematics. This apparently commonsense view is a little difficult to explain or to justify. Potential is a somewhat nebulous attribute, because, as soon as it is translated into identifiable skills or abilities, it becomes achievement. Perhaps the disparity is that some children who appear articulate and intelligent in their conversation and everyday behaviour do not perform well in school mathematics. It may be that they do not respond well to the experiences and activities through which they are expected to learn mathematics, or that the forms of assessment adopted in this subject do not provide them with the opportunity to demonstrate their ability.

The best documented aspect of underachievement in mathematics is the difference between boys and girls. There is no obvious reason why boys should have an inherent advantage in learning mathematics, and yet, over the years, evidence of such a gender difference has accumulated. Perhaps school mathematics has been presented in a way which, for whatever reason, is accepted more favourably by boys. Similarly, it may well be that the mathematics curriculum has appeared less relevant or less appropriate to pupils from certain cultural or ethnic backgrounds. These considerations suggest that there are large categories of pupils whose needs in school mathematics should be given more careful analysis, and the next two chapters deal with these broad categories.

Gender and multicultural issues have been given quite a lot of emphasis in educational literature. Yet there are plenty of pupils who appear to need something different from a standard diet of secondary mathematics if their potential is to be realised, for reasons other than those of gender and ethnic origin. These include 'gifted' children who show a much greater level of achievement than their contemporaries in mathematics, as well as less able children who do not appear to have the capacity to match the level of competence of most of their peers. There are children who, because of some specific disability, may need different kinds of help and teaching and learning from the majority. There may also be those whose preferred way of working or style of thinking is not well served by the activities provided in mathematics classes.

MATHEMATICALLY GIFTED CHILDREN

It is difficult to determine whether, and to what extent, there can be such a thing as specific mathematical ability. As described in Chapter 1, mathematical competence is made up of a variety of different aspects, which are present in different forms in other school subjects. In some fields of human activity, such as music and art, there is a strong belief that some children have a natural talent which, if nurtured, can lead to high individual achievement. There are teachers who would go some way towards expressing a similar view of mathematics, and yet, more often than not, ability in mathematics is seen as a reflection of general intelligence.

Straker (1983), surveying research in this area, explains that the usual conclusion is that children who are good at mathematics are above average also in general intelligence: a rather weak statement of this nature is about all that can be claimed. There are some children who put a lot of effort into mathematics, and achieve results in this subject which are not reflected in other aspects of their work in school. A more familiar anomaly is the lack of achievement in mathematics of some people who in other respects show a high level of general intelligence. It seems possible that these discrepancies are indicative of particular affective responses to mathematics and to the way it is presented, rather than of intellectual strength or weakness. Whatever the reason, the evidence is that high achievement in mathematics is often associated with generally good performance in school work, but that sometimes it is not.

It may seem a little odd that the existence of pupils who have a particular strength in mathematics, and who can cope easily with the normal demands of the school curriculum, is seen as a problem. Yet giftedness is commonly described in this way: Straker and others take the view that, unless teachers are aware of and broadly sympathetic to this 'problem', the provision of appropriate education for gifted children is difficult. An HMI survey (1977) reported a variety of attitudes to very able children, sometimes including indifference and even hostility to any special recognition. Perhaps there is some feeling that schools should serve a compensatory function, and lavish greater attention on those who are not achieving very much and for that reason need the most help. A more positive view, however, is that particular strengths and abilities should be encouraged and developed wherever this is possible. The hope must then be that special talents will be used to benefit the wider population.

If no special consideration is given to the needs of the most able children, then, if a text or scheme is followed slavishly, such pupils are hardly likely to find school mathematics satisfying. Material produced with the majority of children in mind will contain work which is routine and even trivial for the more able: it may lead to a perception of mathematics as a boring, sterile subject. With formal, whole-class teaching, however, the situation may be even worse. The difficulties of presenting the same material to pupils of a broad range of ability were highlighted in Chapter 10, and the most able children in a group can sometimes spend all their time 'learning' mathematics which they already know and working on exercises which make no new demands on them.

Inevitably, because of the pressures and forms of organisation in secondary schools, teachers are often ready to look for an even and uniform rate of progress amongst pupils. Lack of conformity on the part of individual children may not only make life difficult for the teacher, but can also create friction and be regarded as deviant amongst other pupils in the class. This tension is a risk for any children whose abilities or needs differ markedly in some way from those of the majority of their peers. The pressure to conform is strong, but gifted children in particular need the freedom to develop individual ideas and pursue their own lines of work.

One strategy which has occasionally been adopted is 'acceleration': gifted children are pushed through the educational system at a faster rate than others. Over the years, many selective schools in particular have adopted procedures which allow a group of pupils to embark on an A-level course a year early, after 4 years of secondary schooling rather than 5. This is a relatively gentle kind of acceleration. More drastically, there have been cases of children who have taken A-level mathematics successfully at a very early age, and even gone on to study for a university degree while still in their early teens. Although these are a small number of isolated cases, they have been given a lot of publicity by the media. Evidence of the enormous range of ability in mathematics suggests that rather more children could be accelerated in this way. Such a strategy effectively abandons any real attempt at conformity and takes the children concerned away from peer group pressures and conventional school structures. Even for an obviously gifted pupil, most parents and teachers would probably reject such a notion for social reasons, without giving it serious consideration as a path to intellectual achievement.

Schools which adopt schemes designed to cater for mixed-ability groups commit themselves, in effect, to a form of individualised work which allows very able pupils to progress at a faster rate. This form of acceleration is of dubious value, however, in that it results simply in more rapid consumption of the material which is provided for everyone. Within individualised learning systems, it is always relatively difficult to organise class and group discussions at a level useful to all pupils, and it is especially difficult to provide for gifted pupils in this respect. In any case, mixed-ability grouping is normally designed to keep children of the same age together regardless of ability, so that, if the very able work right through the entire scheme in a short time, new additional work has then to be provided.

All these considerations lead to the conclusion that, for most pupils who are particularly able in mathematics, suitable enrichment activity needs to be available within the everyday classroom context. This may be provided in a number of different ways. For example, pupils may be required to tackle more difficult problems in a given topic, or work in greater depth on an investigation, which is being provided in some form for the whole class. Alternatively, mathematically able pupils may have their work broadened to include additional topics outside the usual syllabus.

Some schemes include enrichment activities for more able pupils as part of the published resources. Straker (1983) provides some useful suggestions, and the books by Bolt (1982, 1985, 1987) include some activities which can be used as enrichment in this way. Indeed, there are many books of mathematical puzzles, activities and diversions which can be useful resources; but it is difficult to choose and predict exactly which activity is likely to prove a rich starting point for mathematical work for an individual, able pupil. This choice, however, is often best left to the pupil: the most appropriate role for teachers in providing enrichment activity for gifted children is to point out sources of interesting material and give opportunities for discussion, rather than deciding exactly what work such children ought to do.

The increased use of microcomputers in school mathematics has brought many opportunities for exciting work with more able pupils. Here again, some care is needed in identifying useful software which can provide scope for the innovative thinking of which mathematically gifted pupils may be capable. Perhaps more than other children, the most able are capable of challenging the belief that mathematics is about solving other people's problems. To this end, software is needed which asks no questions but puts the onus on the user to frame ideas and identify problems and activities. Townsend (1987), in discussing this aspect of computer work, describes the use of LOGO as the ultimate in giving the control back to the learner, but there are other computer facilities which share this feature.

Many forms of extracurricular provision have been suggested, and indeed set up, to enrich the experience of mathematically able pupils. These include:

- special extra lessons
- out-of-school visits
- work experience
- short residential courses
- mathematics clubs
- displays or exhibitions
- the production of a magazine or periodical
- competitions and contests

Inevitably, such special arrangements are not easy to provide: they demand time, effort and enthusiasm from teachers, who may in other respects feel constrained by the requirements of the National Curriculum and GCSE and a variety of other pressures on their work. Catering for the mathematical needs of gifted children remains the concern of a small minority, but it is a world-wide concern. For those who are interested in comparing strategies and approaches to this provision, there is a useful international summary in a special issue of *Educational Studies in Mathematics* (1986).

LOW ATTAINERS IN MATHEMATICS

Over the years there have been a number of projects which have attempted in various ways to identify the needs of low-attaining pupils or to promote good practice in meeting these needs. It is a common conclusion of such projects that this work has relevance to most children – that many of the general difficulties which are identified and the recommendations for good practice have some significance for those teaching mathematics throughout the age and ability range. As a result, books developed from this work are often not specifically concerned with the less able. Thus Dickson *et al.* (1984) have produced a teachers' guide to research which has implications for all teachers of mathematics: this arose out of a low attainer's project funded by the Schools Council at Chelsea College from 1979 to 1982. A further project, funded by the DES and a number of LEAs, and based at West Sussex Institute of Higher Education, was responsible for the curriculum development study *Better Mathematics* (1987), which again aims to encourage and develop general 'good practice' in teaching mathematics.

The experience of these projects suggests what is in any case a very plausible conclusion. The difficulties experienced by less able pupils in mathematics are mostly not very different in kind from those which other pupils have. In all the chapters of this book, pupils' problems and misconceptions of various kinds are identified. On the whole, low-attaining pupils are those who experience more of these difficulties, sometimes in an exaggerated way, and often in entrenched forms which are not easy to correct.

It is this apparent intransigence of the difficulties which a small number of pupils have with almost any mathematics that demands special consideration, and various developments have brought this issue into greater prominence. For one thing, the trend to integrate children who would previously have been allocated to 'special' education into 'normal' schools and ordinary classrooms means that more teachers are likely to meet children with relatively severe learning difficulties. Also the National Curriculum requirements apply, except in very rare cases, to all children, so that the problems cannot be shelved by restricting the mathematics learning of some children to a very narrow and simple diet, even if this were a genuinely effective strategy.

For those teachers who want to explore the issues in more detail, there are a number of books available. Denvir *et al.* (1982), in their report of the Chelsea low attainers' project, present an overview of policies in schools, and evaluate different classroom practices. Larcombe (1985) concentrates both on the needs of pupils who experience particular difficulties in school mathematics and on the role of the teacher in meeting these needs.

The Education Reform Act of 1988 gave to all pupils the statutory right to a broad, balanced and differentiated curriculum relevant to their needs. This has been presented as a recognition of the pressure for equal opportunities, which was encouraged by the integration aims of the 1981 Education Act. Establishing the principle, and making the appropriate provision to translate it into practice, are, however, two different matters. Guidelines on this are given by the National Curriculum Council's (1989) booklet *A Curriculum for All*.

In terms of its implications for ordinary schools, this document emphasises the need to make curriculum breadth accessible to all pupils. It suggests that schools need to check their curriculum plans, asking whether they ensure that:

- all staff know which pupils have special educational needs, the nature of their needs and how best to meet these needs;
- maximum access and progress for pupils with special educational needs are possible;
- adequate resources, support and training are available to staff;
- a designated member of staff is responsible for co-ordinating a school-wide policy for special educational needs;
- the effects of the National Curriculum on pupils with special educational needs can be monitored and evaluated.

In special schools, it is suggested that the emphasis will have to be on extending their curricular breadth. Plans should, wherever possible, include links with nearby ordinary schools. Such links are intended both to extend the special schools' subject range and to aim at a compatibility which will make it easier for pupils to move into the mainstream.

The need to broaden the curriculum for pupils with special education needs is a general one, but the need to broaden the curriculum within mathematics for low-attaining pupils is an important aspect of this. There is some evidence that the mathematics curriculum for the less able has often been deliberately narrowed, both in subject content and in the kind of learning expected:

- it has largely consisted of arithmetic;
- it has concentrated on skills, usually taught and learned in a very instrumental way.

Denvir *et al.* (1982) report how their project team found low attainers in the third and fourth year of secondary schools spending most of their time trying to master the same arithmetical skills which younger low attainers worked on in junior schools. Similarly, an HMI survey (1979) discovered that the teacher's response to weakness was often a concentration on teaching standard procedures, even though this emphasis on skill devoid of application or motivation was generally counter-productive.

One explanation of the temptation to teach closely defined algorithmic techniques to children whose competence in mathematics is low is that such techniques are apparently easy to teach. Tasks can be broken up into easy stages, precise rules can be given, and children have only to follow instructions in order to achieve success. Unfortunately, the success is likely to prove transitory and illusory. Instrumental learning of techniques relies strongly on memory, and low attainers are hardly likely to retain skills which are unrelated to their established ideas and activities. Also, divorced of any context in which they are applied and understood, skills are of no great value.

Sometimes there has been considerable emotional pressure to succeed in standard forms of arithmetic. This has been seen by some teachers as the 'normal' basis of success in mathematics, so that enormous efforts have been made to give children with severe learning difficulties some skill in this area – and the tiniest achievement has been regarded as reason for delight and rejoicing. Like many other aspects of special education, this attitude can also be considered sad, or even cruel, depending on your perspective.

Returning to the development of skills, and in particular to the possibility of breaking up activities into easy, small stages, the National Curriculum Council booklet offers a number of questions about schemes of work as they relate to pupils with special needs. These questions include:

> Can the activities be broken down into series of small and achievable steps for pupils who have marked learning difficulties?

Without much more detailed discussion, this somewhat simplistic question is a little unfortunate. It clearly expects the answer 'yes', and encourages teachers to try to break down activities in this way. Yet, there is a contradictory view. Trickett and Sulke (1988), for example, identify four common actions which *inhibit* pupils' mathematical development. The first two of these are:

- The subject is broken down into 'easily digestible topics'.
- There is an over-concern to simplify, by breaking general ideas into seemingly unrelated stages.

In reality, there is sufficient evidence to show that low-attaining children have a better chance to flourish when their experience of mathematics is broadened both in terms of content and in the style of learning expected of them. Trickett and Sulke refer to 'remarkable results' achieved with children from mainstream and special schools when mathematics teaching has been opened up to allow pupils to find their own strategies and solutions. This freedom needs to be developed in a supportive environment, so that challenge, frustration and struggle can be appreciated as intrinsic and sometimes positive aspects of learning mathematics.

The *Proceedings of the Sixth International Congress on Mathematical Education* include a section on the problems of handicapped students (Csocsan 1988). Among the papers summarised there, from many countries, are several which describe successful developments in broadening the mathematical experience of children whose previous learning was restricted to simple arithmetic work in special education. It is regrettable that much of this work has not been published in detail for a wider, international readership. However, the broad conclusions are not really surprising. Children who encounter serious difficulties in learning mathematics are likely to achieve greater success when:

- they are allowed access to a broad variety of topics and activities in mathematics rather than restricted to a narrow, prescriptive set of skills;
- the classroom environment is sufficiently supportive, so that working on tasks perceived as difficult can be regarded as a positive activity;
- individual attention is available for low-attaining pupils when required, so that they have the opportunity to discuss and talk through difficulties.

These considerations justify the decision to make the breadth of the National Curriculum apply to all pupils, including the least able. They also provide encouragement for policies of integration, so long as pupils with special needs can be accepted and have their needs respected both by teachers and by their classmates. Furthermore, the use of extra support teachers to work with children with special needs in ordinary classrooms is likely to prove beneficial and is sometimes essential.

The use of ancillary and teaching support for children with special needs has grown in recent years. It is generally regarded with positive enthusiasm and there is much anecdotal` evidence of its effectiveness, although it would be difficult to provide a systematic evaluation of this trend. Bowes *et al.* (1988) describe support work in the mathematics classroom from the point of view of the class teacher, the support teacher and the pupil. Their story demonstrates open-mindedness on all their parts; and, in that context, their development from tentative unease to confident acceptance of the arrangement is reassuringly predictable.

The magazine *Struggle*, in which this story appears, has for several years been concerned specifically with the mathematical needs of low attainers. Originally produced by the Inner London Education Authority, it is now published jointly by the Mathematical Association and the National Association for Remedial Education. Its particular value is in its descriptions of activities which have been tried and found effective in working with low attainers in the classroom.

PUPILS WITH PHYSICAL DISABILITIES

One effect of the trend towards integration is that teachers in ordinary schools are rather more likely to have disabled pupils in their classes. Children who are blind or partially sighted, deaf or to some extent hearing-impaired and those with restricted mobility learn mathematics along with others of their own age. Such pupils have obvious 'special needs'. In most mathematics lessons, pupils have to look at books or worksheets or whatever is written on a board, to listen to the teacher or to one another, and often to move around the classroom or the school in order to become involved in the activity. Special arrangements, possibly including the provision of technical aids or even in some cases radical reorganisation of the classroom arrangement, can be, are and must be made to accommodate children with particular disabilities.

This, however, may not be the whole of the story. The reports from ICME 6 (Csocsan 1988) include some work which suggests that 'probably, all disabled persons are handicapped in their mathematical learning to some extent'. This is a dangerous and provocative statement. It carries the risk that disabled people will be labelled – that teachers' expectations of pupils' potential in mathematics will be low, because of those pupils' physical disabilities. In this context, it is important to keep in mind that some blind people, deaf people and some severely handicapped by cerebral palsy, for example, have obtained degrees in mathematics and achieved considerable academic success.

On the other hand, it has to be recognised that disabled pupils inevitably do not have the same range of physical and sensory experiences to draw on as their able-bodied counterparts. Mathematics teaching – especially good mathematics teaching – relies very much on children's everyday experience. It needs only a little extra thought to realise that for the disabled this experience is restricted in very specific ways.

Sometimes perceived restrictions on experience are less obvious and their validity can be questioned. *A Curriculum for All*, in the section on mathematics, suggests that the pupil confined to a wheelchair may have had limited opportunities to play and work with a group of peers and will particularly benefit from collaborative tasks. As a generalisation, there is no doubt some truth in this, but plenty of children in wheelchairs will have had opportunities of this kind. Also, there are plenty of other factors which tend to restrict social collaboration: isolated housing, for example, or even being an only child.

Visual handicap is most obviously an impediment to learning in spatial aspects of mathematics – those topics concerned with geometry or graphical work. Tactile diagrams and graphs can be produced, but in many cases graphical methods may not be the most appropriate for blind people. After all, graphs are often designed to enable sighted people to understand more clearly, or analyse more easily, some numerical information. Perhaps a different form of presentation should be developed for blind pupils. Many sighted mathematicians are accustomed to thinking in graphical terms, and it takes a leap of imagination to contemplate introducing calculus, for example, without the visual aid which the graph of a function provides.

In work with number, visual impairment has less obvious disadvantages. Yet, especially in investigations, we talk about 'looking' for a pattern in an array of numbers. The privilege of setting out a set of numbers, or any other objects for that matter, in some particular format, and then scanning them for a pattern, is available only to sighted people. Csocsan (1988), discussing blind children's formation of basic mathematical concepts and their models and perceptions of such concepts, questions whether the idea of a 'set' can or should be so fundamental as it is with sighted pupils. Seeing a whole set at once and recognising number in that context is just not available. Alternative ways of developing awareness of pattern and understanding of number, based on operations and functions, might be developed, and could perhaps be more appropriate.

Nott (1988) provides some interesting comments on mathematical work with visually impaired children. Her description of a 10 year old who attempted to estimate the area of the classroom floor, having no idea that it was covered with square plastic tiles, is just one example of insight at a very basic level. In the same journal, Steel (1988) offers some suggestions for equipment and materials which might be useful in teaching mathematics to pupils with limited vision.

Quite a lot has been written about the particular problems experienced by hearing-impaired children in mathematics, compared with normally hearing children. Watts (1979) attaches great importance to the difficulties of deaf children in learning multiplication tables. Probably, like a lot of aspects of work with the disabled, the real difficulty lies not in the mathematics itself but in the way teachers and parents believe tables should 'normally' be learned. Most people remember the answer to multiplication questions by association of the sounds (seven fives?) – a facility which is not available to deaf people. Again, an alternative approach is needed.

Barham (1988) draws attention to an insistence by most teachers of deaf children that language is the cause of the deaf child's difficulty with mathematics. There is some evidence that this is a valid view: Wildig (quoted in Csocsan 1988) also cites restricted language skills as a significant factor in the low attainment of most deaf children in mathematics. Some attempts to meet the needs of deaf pupils and to find ways of minimising their language difficulties in learning mathematics have been made by the Mathematics for the Deaf Child

Project set up at the Cambridge University Department of Education in 1984. Its strategies include the development and evaluation of suitable computer software for deaf children.

It is a reflection of the adaptability (some would say, the long-suffering tolerance) of teachers in secondary schools that most are ready to welcome the integration of pupils with special needs and, however uneasy they might be about unfamiliar problems, are prepared to be sensitive and sympathetic. All teachers occasionally catch themselves saying something which suddenly seems inappropriate. Asking blind children whether they can 'see' a pattern of relationship is one common example; trying to explain positive and negative numbers in terms of taking 'steps' forward and back to pupils in wheelchairs is another. Such experiences probably embarrass teachers more than pupils: after all, disabled people are used to a world not designed for their benefit and meet such nonsense every day of their lives.

On the other hand, other forms of insensitivity may be more upsetting. Neurological clumsiness, for example, is a very common feature of physical disability, and may result in pupils being very slow at recording and producing untidy written work. It is of little use to such pupils to be told repeatedly to get a move on, or that their work is not neat enough to be acceptable. The guidance from the National Curriculum Council is helpful in this respect in recommending the use of technological aids, including, for example, the provision of a word processor where appropriate.

For most disabled pupils, the provision of technological aids does not remove the need for personal support in the classroom, whether from a support teacher or an ancillary helper. It is, however, the general view that technology can give such pupils increased independence. It seems likely that our response to disability in education in Britain will be an increasing reliance on technology. If we were asked to plan for a blind or deaf student or someone unable to write to enter higher education, for instance, our immediate response would probably be to ask what technical equipment might enable the student to cope with the course. In other parts of the world, the more likely strategy might be to appoint a part-time helper or personal amanuensis to attend classes with the student, taking notes and helping in whatever way was necessary. We should probably claim that our approach gives greater independence to the student, but why is dependence on technology more acceptable than dependence on another person? The value judgment may be a cultural one, but it could also be economic. In present-day Britain, compared with most of the world, technology is cheap while the salary costs of long-term help are relatively expensive.

COGNITIVE STYLES AND STRATEGIES

The section of the review of research by Bell *et al.* (1983) concerned with individual differences is almost entirely about cognitive styles. It reflects the scant attention given to any consideration of personality characteristics in the literature of mathematics education. Head (1981) draws attention to the lack of evidence or understanding of any clear link between personality variables and performance in mathematics, even though there is a popular assumption that personality variables play some role, especially in motivation and the formation of attitudes.

Furthermore, since 1983 there has been relatively little development of the work on the relationship between cognitive style and learning mathematics. It has not been a fasionable field for research. For these reasons, the issues are not well explored, but two ideas are worth consideration. One is that pupils' success or failure in mathematics can sometimes be explained in terms of the match or mismatch between their preferred style of thinking and learning and the kind of behaviour which is expected of them in mathematics lessons. The mismatch may be, for example, between reflective and impulsive styles; or it may be in the holist–serialist dimension suggested by Pask (1976). A second notion is that an extreme bias in pupils' style of thinking might make them very likely to make errors in tasks of a particular kind: a high degree of field dependence might be one example of such a bias.

The distinction between reflective and impulsive thinking is a plausible one. There are people who like to reflect carefully before committing themselves, and who prefer to take extra time rather than risk making a mistake. In contrast, others prefer to respond impulsively even at the risk of error, and have little patience with careful, reflective behaviour. Perhaps this could be seen as a difference in cognitive pace rather than style.

Teachers can create a classroom environment in which either an impulsive or a reflective style of behaviour is encouraged. Quickfire questions demand impulsive responses, while the contrasting style allows pauses for reflection and analysis. It is easy to imagine a naturally impulsive pupil being bored and impatient with a lesson which demands reflective behaviour. On the other hand, the more reflective pupil is even less likely to be able to cope with demands for impulsive thinking. There are some studies of such mismatches in classrooms – Radatz (1979) quotes a number of examples, including the following description of a reflective pupil by an impulsive teacher:

> ... he does not say much, no reactions, seems to dream very often – funny, by chance he comes out with a marvellous contribution – his neighbour must have prompted him!

In discussing holism and serialism, Pask (1976) does not present these as cognitive styles but as alternative learning strategies. Holism involves the attempt to achieve a global description or understanding of a system or structure, while serialism concentrates on one goal at a time, resulting in the mastery of topics in a step-by-step fashion. In learning mathematics, the comparable choice might be between trying first to understand the overall structure of a system or topic and then developing procedures for working within this structure based on understanding; or starting by learning a range of specific facts, skills and techniques within a topic and gradually building up a broader understanding later if required. These are recognisable alternative approaches to learning, and indeed to teaching, particular mathematical topics.

It is likely, however, that some pupils have a predisposition towards an approach which seeks to convey global understanding of a topic (in Pask's terms, 'comprehension learners') while others prefer the step-by-step serialist approach ('operation learners'). There are those who are able to act in either way according to the kind of learning outcome desired – such pupils are called 'versatile'. Both styles of learning have some place in school mathematics but the suggestion here is that some individuals perceive learning mostly as a general construction of structural relationships, while others are mainly concerned with developing particular skills. Pupils may of course develop these perceptions as a result of previous educational experiences, but, however the predilection has been created, some pupils will be disadvantaged by teaching approaches which emphasise one particular kind of learning rather than the other.

Field dependence is one aspect of cognitive style which might be offered as an explanation of differences in performance in mathematics and of some pupils' difficulties with certain tasks. Perhaps the test of field dependence which is closest to any aspect of school mathematics is the embedded-figures task described by Witkin (1977). In the diagram below, the simple figure on the left has to be located within the complex figure on the right:

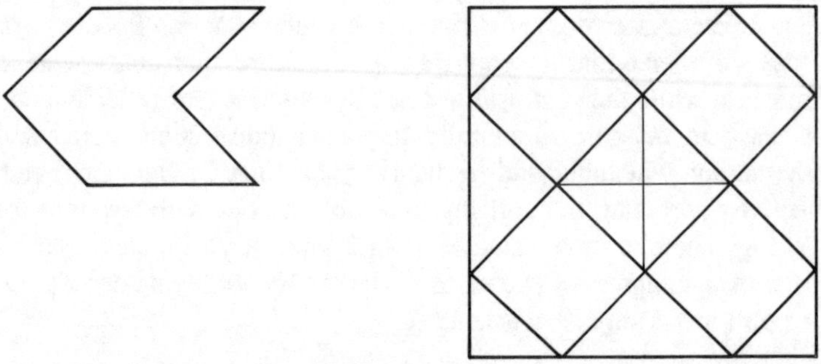

For some ('field-independent') people, the sought-after shape quickly emerges, while others are unable to find it in the minute or so allowed for the search.

This is one example of a situation in which the detailed features of the surrounding field distract some people completely. It is reminiscent of a number of situations in the literature of mathematics education, some of which have already been mentioned. In Chapter 4, for example, a lot of children were identified as having difficulty comparing lengths of slant lines on rectangular grids.

These situations both involve some error caused by the distraction of the field. Similar considerations may offer a rationalisation of the way in which some people are more easily fooled than others by so-called 'optical illusions'.

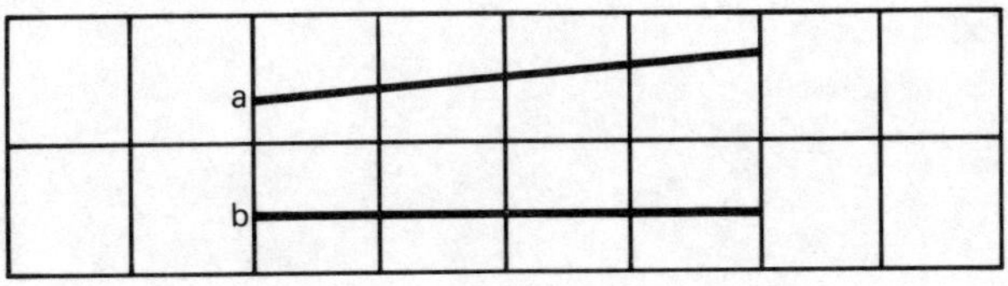

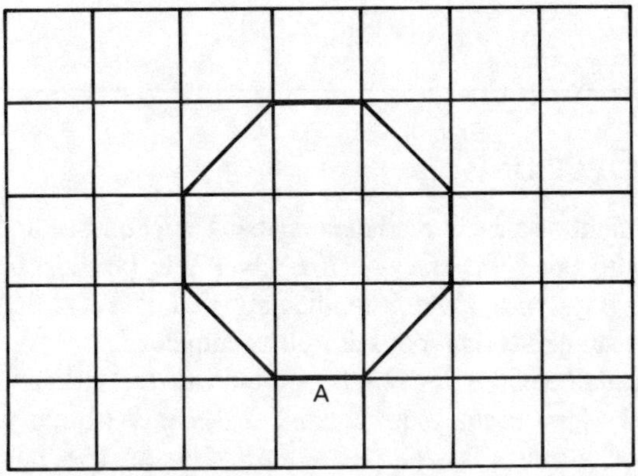

A different kind of field distraction is provided by elaborate word problems in which a particular numerical operation or relationship has to be identified. While the level of difficulty of such problems depends on several factors, as described in Chapter 2, they do prove rather more difficult for some pupils than others. Some are easily led astray by false cues and information.

The idea of field dependence or independence is an interesting one, and can be applied to a variety of situations. It offers a possible model to explain differences in performance, but its implications have to be considered in terms of specific tasks. It does not have any easy or obvious implications for the appropriate choice of teaching style.

CONCLUSIONS

This chapter is a collection of disparate themes which are not easy to summarise. The common thread, however, is that children are not all the same. They differ in what they learn, how they learn and the rate at which they learn.

For the teacher, the message is one of open-mindedness and flexibility. Complete fairness is an ideal but not a practicable objective, and it will never be possible to organise the teaching of mathematics to take account of every child's precise, individual requirements. It is important to recognise the value of variety, however, and to be aware that persisting with a narrowly consistent style will be disadvantageous to a proportion of childen.

Chapter 15

Gender differences in learning mathematics

DIFFERENCES IN PARTICIPATION

The participation and achievement of girls in mathematics has been an issue and a cause for concern in Britain since the early 1970s. Over this period, the evidence that fewer girls than boys participate in mathematics courses and that girls on average achieve lower standards than boys is well documented.

Officially, participation in mathematics lessons is compulsory for girls and boys alike, and the National Curriculum requirements make this statutory. Furthermore, the existence of a single system of examination at 16+ has, superficially at least, removed the differentiated entry to O-level and CSE mathematics. Throughout the currency of these separate examinations, more boys were entered for O-level and more girls for CSE; and, although the imbalance was reduced over the years, it showed no sign of disappearing altogether. Some differentiation continues to exist because of the choice of taking GCSE papers at three different levels: it remains to be seen how far girls and boys will be treated differently in this respect over the years, and indeed how the disadvantaged position of girls might show up in the assessment procedures of the National Curriculum.

It is at higher levels, however, that the participation of women is significantly curtailed. More than twice as many boys as girls take A-level mathematics, and women are under-represented in almost all courses with a strong mathematical element in higher education.

DIFFERENCES IN ACHIEVEMENT

The evidence is clear that there are differences in achievement in mathematics between girls and boys. These differences begin in the primary school. It is sometimes claimed that at that stage the differences are minimal and that the manifestly greater success which boys enjoy develops during adolescence. It is true that some surveys which test children's performance across a wide range of mathematical topics at age 10 or 11 appear to show little difference between the sexes. This overall equality, however, masks enormous variations in success on particular tasks and topics: a detailed summary of these variations based mainly on information from Ward (1979) and the APU (1985) is provided by Shuard (in Burton, 1986).

Girls do significantly better than boys, for example, on questions demanding computational skill, especially when a particular style of setting out is expected:

$$315 \div 6$$

Write down and work out this division sum.

At this stage, boys do better on a range of tasks, including in particular those concerned with measurement and problem-solving. A number of statements have been made by various authors and commentators to try to describe concisely the nature and significance of these differences. Such explanations include the following:

- By the end of primary school, boys are ahead in those aspects of mathematics which are a fruitful basis for future understanding and development.
- Tests which cover the range of mathematical activity in primary school hide the extent of differences between boys and girls, and tests which favour computation rather than problem-solving give an over-optimistic picture of girls' potential in mathematics.
- The questions on which girls perform better are:
  (a) easier;
  (b) given more attention in the classroom; and
  (c) considered more important by teachers.

There is a somewhat disturbing sub-text behind much of this analysis. It suggests that the emphasis of much primary mathematics may not be the best basis for future success in the subject, and that girls may disadvantage themselves by giving greater credence to their teachers' views and priorities in this respect.

Experience from all the APU surveys indicates that, by the age of 15, boys have a higher average level of achievement than girls in all aspects of the mathematics curriculum: they obtain higher average results on almost every written test. Again the difference is most marked in work in the measures category.

The most striking difference in achievement both in primary and secondary school is to be found in the highest attainment band. The APU surveys show a much higher proportion of boys than girls in the top 10 per cent of attainers in mathematics at both age 11 and age 15. This under-representation of girls at the highest level of achievement is reflected in GCSE and A-level results: at A-level especially, a considerably higher percentage of boys than girls entered for the mathematics examination achieve a grade A pass. It is important to recognise, however, that the imbalance in the top attainment band remains inadequate as an explanation of the differentiated entry at A-level. Over the years, of all pupils who have obtained a grade A pass in mathematics at O-level or GCSE, a much higher percentage of boys than girls have gone on to study the subject at A-level. It seems likely that the choice of subjects at A-level is based at least as much on affective factors as levels of achievement, and also that the criteria for advising pupils about their choice may be different for boys and girls.

DIFFERENCES IN ATTITUDE

As indicated in Chapter 13, the APU surveys contain extensive information about children's attitudes, both to mathematics as a whole and to different topics within mathematics. Amongst 11-year-old children, there is little difference between the sexes in their overall response to statements about the interest, difficulty or usefulness of mathematics. There is some evidence at this stage that girls are more likely to express uncertainty about their opinion. This unwillingness to articulate a clear view is established firmly during the secondary school years, and, in general, when girls are asked to rate statements they are inclined to make moderate assessments. Girls use the extreme positive and negative positions on opinion scales far more reluctantly than boys do.

During the secondary school years, girls' attitudes to mathematics deteriorate rather more than those of boys. Although doubts may be expressed about the usefulness of some topics, it is clear that belief in the importance of mathematics for future life stands up relatively well and has some motivating influence regardless of whether the subject is considered difficult or interesting. Even here, however, by age 15 boys are more inclined to rate mathematics as useful than girls are.

Amongst 15 year olds, the largest sex difference in attitudes is in pupils' views of the difficulty of mathematics. Girls are far more likely to express the view that mathematics is difficult than boys are. This difference in attitude is an exaggeration of the difference in performance. Boys tend to underrate the level of difficulty, and overrate their own competence: they frequently do less well than they expect. Girls are more likely to overrate the difficulty and devalue their own expertise: they often achieve better results than they expect. The work by Thomas and Costello (1988) described in Chapter 13, which identifies good experiences of school mathematics reported by girls, highlights the high incidence of situations where girls expect failure and are surprised by success.

The differential mismatch between perceived difficulty and level of competence is neatly illustrated by one example from the APU surveys, quoted by Joffe and Foxman (in Burton 1986). In the item opposite, 48 per cent of boys and 42 per cent of girls gave the correct answer.

When asked how easy or difficult it was, 51 per cent of boys and 38 per cent of girls said it was easy – more boys and fewer girls than were able to give the correct answer.

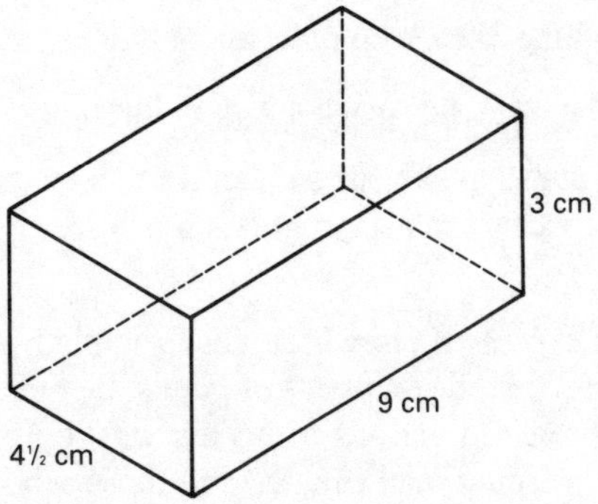

What is the volume of this rectangular block? ....cm^3.

Apart from differences in their opinions, which can be canvassed in this way, there are less easily identified differences between boys and girls in their emotional response to mathematics and in their perception of what the subject is about. Mathematics can generate intense anxiety amongst pupils, and girls appear more vulnerable to this than boys. This can have the effect of discouraging girls from making a contribution to discussion for fear of showing up their own inadequacies. The emphasis given by girls to computational skill, especially at the upper primary school level, and their relative success in this area, may be an indication of a tendency for girls to regard the topic as the central concern of mathematics. On the other hand, all these matters may be indicative of gender differences in cognitive style: this is a notion which has had little attention.

PUPILS' PERCEPTIONS OF GENDER DIFFERENCES

In spite of the evidence of greater participation by men than women in mathematical activity, of the greater success of boys than girls in mathematics tests and examination, and of girls' less favourable attitude to the subject, many pupils do not see differences in these terms. The APU 1982 survey of 15 year olds (APU 1985) includes a section in which pupils were asked in detail about sex differences in mathematical achievement. A large proportion of both boys and girls claimed that there were no differences; and, amongst those who believed that differences exist, opinion was almost equally divided as to which sex is superior. Some pupils' comments on the matter are quoted by Joffe and Foxman (in Burton 1986).

(Boy) The girls tend to get better results because they seem to be able to concentrate more.

(Girl) Girls do best. Most of the boys mess around.

(Boy) If some girls do not know something, they keep quiet about it.

(Boy) When a boy is asked what a question is, he answers it straightaway.

(Boy) ... when you ask a girl a maths question she takes about 5 minutes to answer it. ... Boys do more complicated jobs than girls – a boy learns easier as well.

Some of these remarks echo the opinions expressed elsewhere, for example by Spender and Sarah (1981). In a lot of these reported comments of pupils, there is an identifiable, common feature which appears in various forms amongst both those who believe that girls are better at learning mathematics and those who think that boys have the advantage. This prevalent impression is that boys have the confidence to answer immediately and often impulsively or spontaneously in class, whereas girls are more careful, conscientious, meticulous and perhaps reflective. Whether this distinction is valid or not, it is clear that a lot of pupils in secondary school would concur with an opinion of this kind. Interestingly this can make them believe that girls are better at maths or that boys are better. Perhaps the remarks tell us more about what pupils think being good at mathematics requires rather than their perceptions of gender differences in learning mathematics.

DIFFERENCES IN COGNITIVE STYLE

Scott-Hodgetts (in Burton 1986) offers some exploration of the view that gender differences in learning mathematics may be associated with differences in cognitive style. Her hypothesis is that people who are inclined to adopt a serialist approach to learning are disadvantaged when learning mathematics, and that a greater proportion of girls than boys exhibit serialist preferences.

In one sense, the pattern of development of the mathematical performance of girls supports the view that this is linked to a serialist tendency. The form in which computational arithmetic is presented in primary schools lends itself very much to an instrumental style of learning, and we might expect a serialist approach to be successful. Also, it is predictable that serialists should fall behind as conceptual structures become more complex, so that understanding of relationships becomes central to success. Furthermore it might be expected that this would be most significant at the top of the ability range, and it is here that the ratio of boys to girls is high.

The notion of cognitive style, however, provides us with another alternative way of characterising gender differences in learning mathematics. Most items on which girls achieve higher average scores than boys in tests in primary school are relatively easy. Now difficult items, on which both sexes score low, demand insight and understanding – but easy test items demand care. If reasonably competent pupils fail on difficult items, this is likely to indicate lack of understanding, while failure on an easy item (especially in computational arithmetic) is more likely to be a mistake.

This might suggest that boys are less careful and more impulsive than girls – that the main difference in style is in the reflective/impulsive dimension. Such a hypothesis is consistent with many pupils' view of how boys and girls behave in mathematics lessons. It also offers an explanation for some other aspects of gender differences, including the common belief, for which there is some evidence, that girls may perform better than boys in coursework but less well in unseen, timed examinations.

ORIGINS AND CAUSES OF GENDER DIFFERENCES

It is perhaps worth dismissing first of all any suggestion that there might be inherent (innate or biological) reasons why boys should be better than girls at learning mathematics. A number of quasi-biological theories have at times been offered as explanations: they are mainly concerned with differences in spatial visualisation. Appendix 2 of the Cockcroft Report (1982) refers briefly to some such theories, which consider, for example, genetic factors, hormonal influences or differences in brain lateralisation to be significant.

These theories are not well articulated, and they have no credibility as explanations of differences in learning mathematics for a variety of reasons. For one thing, competence in mathematics does not demand a single consistent kind of learning: it is a rich mixture of abilities as discussed in Chapter 1. If biological differences affected girls' performance to any real extent in this mixture, they might be expected to impair their intellectual achievement to a similar degree across most of the curriculum. Also, although gender differences exist in many countries and cultures, they are not the same kinds of differences, and they are very much more marked in some countries than others. Such considerations point to social and cultural factors as the determinants of gender differences in education.

From earliest childhood, the experiences which the world provides for girls and boys are different. They are given different toys, adults react to them in different ways, and characteristics thought to be appropriate to their sex are recognised and reinforced. By the time girls reach the infant school, their patterns of behaviour are well established. They regularly choose to play in the 'Wendy House' rather than choose Lego or other constructional toys, they like pretty clothes, and they ask for dolls as presents. In many cases, they have a much clearer and much narrower idea of what they expect from life than boys. Already, they are likely to think in terms of marriage and children, and when asked about jobs, to mention teaching or nursing or being a secretary or working in a shop. The activities which they choose give them less opportunity to explore mathematical relationships than those chosen by boys, and even their classroom discussion is less likely to focus on mathematical tasks.

Gender roles in children's play are more deeply entrenched than many teachers suppose. Taylor (in Burton 1986) describes attempts to encourage girls to take part in a wider range of activities in an infant school. Yet even when groups of girls played regularly with Lego, for example, their style remained different from that of the boys. Boys constructed a greater variety of models, planned and predicted what would happen as they built, and talked themselves through the activity. Girls behaved quite differently. Usually they made houses. They sat down and started the construction in an unplanned way, usually chatting together about something quite different. Relatively quickly, they claimed to have finished or to be bored, and moved on to something else.

A lot of the books which pupils come across in schools reinforce their stereotyped views of male and female behaviour. They show men in active, dynamic roles, and women in passive roles, often in domestic situations. Mathematics textbooks are no better than other publications in this respect, although it is to be hoped that increased awareness will lead those responsible to choose less sexist books for use in school.

Many teachers, often unconsciously, reinforce and validate pupils' perceptions of appropriate gender-related behaviour. They may expect certain forms of assertive behaviour from boys and be prepared for them, thus encouraging a view that acceptable standards are not the same for boys and girls. There is evidence too that teachers react differently to good work in mathematics from boys and girls. A boy who does well is more likely to be told that he has a real talent for mathematics, while a girl is likely to be praised for putting in the hard work needed to produce such a good result. Different standards of presentation of work may also be expected.

During the secondary school years, self-image usually becomes more important for boys and girls alike, and it is often pressure from friends and classmates which determines how this image develops. For many girls, femininity is a priority, and being good at mathematics may well be seen as unfeminine. This is expressed rather disdainfully in some articles, which use slogans such as 'bright girls fear success' or 'nice girls don't do maths'. Such pithy expressions convey the silliness of such views, but the attitudes are neither silly nor trivial to those who suffer from them. For many girls, their view of femininity is a prison. It may be a self-imposed prison, but it is inescapable for all that.

The book by Burton (1986) contains an analysis of the careers advice given to a number of fifth-form girls. It also includes an article by Kelly *et al.* on the establishment of gender roles at home and at school. Like most discussions of gender role socialisation, the present chapter suggests that this is a fairly consistent process to which both home and school contribute. It may be undesirable, but it rarely presents children with contradictory messages. This is not, however, always the view of schools. Many teachers in secondary schools believe strongly that any effect they might wish to promote is likely to be constrained and thwarted by parental opinion. It is expected that such opinion will be largely sex stereotyped.

The picture of parental views which emerges from Kelly *et al.* is an ambivalent one. Parents want their daughters and sons to have access to the same school subjects, and reject the idea that education is more important for boys than for girls. Academic ambition for their children is at least as strong amongst parents of girls as amongst those of boys. When asked about it in such terms, most parents express a commitment to equality between the sexes and approve of the same occupations being open to men and women.

In practice, however, home-based sex stereotypes take a more concrete form. A much higher proportion of girls than boys are likely to be involved in cleaning the house, cooking and washing up, and tidying their own rooms. Girls are also more likely than boys to take part in shopping, washing and mending clothes and laying the table. Equality of education and job opportunities is all very well. Women, it seems, have every right to education and a career, provided they recognise that this does not alter their domestic and maternal role. Kelly expresses it delightfully. Equality, she says, is a little something extra which can be added on to existing social arrangements.

Given all this background, it is inevitable that careers advice for girls is too restricted in scope, too little and too late. Perhaps it is for all pupils. Perhaps careers advice makes little sense in isolation, and what is needed is life advice. Our own little sphere of concern may be to encourage girls to study mathematics, to believe in their own ability in this area and to recognise it as a 'suitable' subject for them. If so, this encouragement has to take place in a social context which puts all kinds of pressures on girls, some of them very much more powerful than anything in mathematics education.

WHY DOES IT MATTER?

Freedom of choice – to study the subjects you want to study, to develop the interests which appeal to you, and to find a career and life-style which suits you – this kind of freedom is wholly positive. Few would disagree, and some would argue that this is what is happening. So what if fewer than half as many girls as boys choose A-level mathematics? What if certain occupations are exclusively male, and others exclusively female? Why does it matter? This is freedom of choice in practice.

If there were a sex-related quota for A-level mathematics entry and the proportion of girls was not allowed to rise, almost everyone would protest. When occupational opportunities have discriminated overtly against women, the right of women to complain has been given overwhelming support. Yet the quota and the occupational barriers exist: they have no statutory framework and they are enforced not by regulation but by an insidious process of attrition to which girls are subjected from the beginning of their lives. The apparent freedom is an illusion, and in some ways the subtlety of the process of female role enforcement makes it all the more disquieting.

Isaacson (in Ernest 1989) refers to this process as 'coercive inducement'. Her perception of this phenomenon is that

> ... girls are persuaded to adopt typically female modes of behaviour and to choose stereotypically feminine occupations, and life styles because the rewards for 'feminine' behaviour are too great to be refused, rather than because they are prevented from choosing others ...

It has to be acknowledged that the idea of femininity and the images and values associated with the idea are very appealing. Taking a pride in yourself and your appearance, wearing pretty clothes, being attractive to other people of both sexes, building up personal relationships and developing a secure and loving domestic life, caring for other people and especially for your own children: who could resist such a package of delights? The package is the problem. It is a take-it-or-leave-it offer: if your self-image is feminine, if you want to be a real woman, these things you must do, and these you must not. Mathematics comes into this because it has a strong male image: Isaacson describes it as 'hard', not so much intellectually difficult but hard as opposed to soft. Mathematics is rigorous, unyielding, unfeminine.

It is very easy for girls and women to learn that large areas of human activity belong to the male domain. The subjects of this domain and the lifestyle and careers they lead to are not for women, and any attempt to enter the domain would be a denial of one's own femininity. This carefully constructed feminine image with its gentleness and its glamour is too precious, and in an odd way too fragile, to be put at risk. The merest suggestion that a particular action might threaten the image is enough to put the action out of bounds. This is how femininity becomes a prison.

None of these comments is intended to decry what are called 'traditional feminine values'. Far from it. What is wrong is that polarised sex stereotyping seeks to label whole ranges of human activity as male or female, and, by so doing, distorts and restricts the opportunities available to everyone in a way which is unnecessary and counter-productive.

The whole issue of women and mathematics has had a high profile in research and other literature in recent years: this is in itself remarkable. There are other areas of the school curriculum which display at least as much gender bias, but receive nothing like the attention. English Literature might be cited as an example. In this case, A-level entries are heavily differentiated in favour of girls, and the disproportion is even greater than in mathematics. Furthermore, there seems little doubt that any survey of lifestyles would reveal a much greater interest in novels and poetry, for example, amongst women compared with men. Yet research has not developed on this: there is no outcry, no campaign to increase the accessibility of English Literature to men.

Presumably mathematics is believed to have an instrumental importance which the study of English Literature does not possess. Competence in mathematics is looked upon as a ticket to opportunities, careers and lifestyles – it leads to status and power. There are underlying assumptions about economic benefit and the national interest here: a numerate population is considered necessary for future prosperity. It is probably this kind of argument which will in the end mobilise powerful support for encouraging girls to study mathematics, rather than concern for the quality of life or equality of opportunity.

STRATEGIES FOR CHANGE

What can be done? Well, some things have been achieved. The proportion of girls continuing to study mathematics after the age of 16 has increased significantly over 20 years. Most teachers are more aware of the dangers of sexism, in books or in classroom practice. Most parents want equality of opportunity for their sons and daughters. On reflection, perhaps that does not seem like a great deal, and it all happens frustratingly slowly. There is a temptation to seek some kind of revolution: a drastic form of intervention which will radically change the behaviour and aspirations of girls.

In one sense, a radical change has happened. Science and technology has become a statutory requirement of the National Curriculum for pupils throughout the 5–16 age range. Girls and boys are forced to have equal access to this area of the curriculum. Especially in the technological aspects, it is hardly true equality. The headstart given to boys by their leisure activities in childhood is not going to go away, and the presence of girls in a classroom does not ensure their active participation. Nevertheless, the decision has been made in principle.

If it is true that some of girls' disadvantage in learning mathematics is attributable to their lack of experience with technical and technological materials, then certainly one possible response is to compensate by providing such material. Give girls sets of Lego and microcomputers and whatever else is felt valuable, and insist that they work with these. Unfortunately, this may not be motivating. The experiences described by Taylor in a previous section show how early in life girls come to reject certain forms of activity as uninteresting and not for them. If change of this kind is to be effective, it may have to go back to early childhood.

Some prominence has been given in the literature to the advantage which girls in single-sex schools have in mathematics compared with those in mixed schools. There is some evidence that girls do indeed achieve a higher level of competence and are more likely to choose to do A-level mathematics in an all-girls school. Also, from the very limited experience which exists of single-sex classes in mixed schools, it seems that there are distinct advantages in grouping girls separately for mathematics. The explanation normally offered is that girls are inhibited in mathematics by the presence of boys: their freedom to flourish is enhanced when this inhibition is removed.

Many people would reject single-sex schooling, and even to an extent single-sex grouping in mathematics, on social grounds which might be seen as more important than possible improvements in mathematical achievement. A lot of pupils, given the choice, would be more concerned about whether they were in the same class as their friends than whether the class was single sex or mixed. The real challenge is to generate a classroom environment which does not inhibit girls in mathematics. If girls can flourish in mathematics when allowed to do so, we should perhaps look for a strategy to re-educate boys in some way to modify their behaviour so as to encourage girls to succeed rather than prevent this.

Careers advice has already been mentioned: it was considered by Cockcroft (1982) a possibly important interventionary strategy. To succeed in this respect, however, careers advice needs to be involved with much wider issues. It needs to address matters of equal opportunity, and to be concerned with pupils' aspirations for their lifestyles in a broader sense than their further education or employment. It probably needs to accept too that a lot of girls will not be swayed from their feminine aspirations. The importance of mathematics needs to be recognised in such areas as the health service, travel, personnel work and teaching, all of which continue to be popular occupations for women. Yet, in all this, careers advisers need to be keen to encourage girls who want to enter careers traditionally considered as 'male'.

There are of course grounds for arguing that coercive pressures operate on boys at least as much as on girls. It may well be that boys have been persuaded to participate in mathematics, science and technology to a much greater degree than they would if they had real freedom of choice. Isaccson (in Burton 1986) quotes some evidence that girls choose A-level mathematics because they enjoy it, while boys are more likely to say that it is expected of them or that it is important for their future. Is it that more boys take mathematics because they are less free than girls to reject it? Gender stereotypes affect both sexes. If such pressures were weakened, options would be chosen more freely. This would mean fewer boys and more girls studying mathematics. Is that our objective?

In practice, the question is academic because stereotypes are not going to go away and can be changed only very slowly. If the dichotomy between mathematics and femininity is the major problem – and it does seem a powerful conflict – then we can work in two ways. We can try to change the vision of femininity to accommodate mathematics, or change the image of mathematics to make it more 'feminine'. Unfortunately, despite the small steps towards progress, some of the most recent developments in mathematics education do not make this reconciliation easier. Computational pencil-and-paper arithmetic – one area in which girls have had an advantage – is much less important. Computers – very much a male preserve – have become an integral part of the mathematics curriculum. In terms of the feminisation of mathematics, these are setbacks.

In spite of all the research and all the initiatives relating to women and mathematics over the last 20 years or so, the conclusion of this chapter must be that we need more. We cannot be happy with pressures which make it difficult for young people to make genuinely free choices. We cannot regard a situation as fair which effectively restricts the opportunities for girls. Yet we should not want to lose many worthwhile 'female' values, attitudes and styles of behaviour: indeed, it would be helpful to find ways of encouraging men to share these. If the price of increasing girls' participation in mathematics is that they should adopt values and styles of behaviour at present more usually associated with men, then many people will feel it is a price not worth paying.

Chapter 16

Cultural and multicultural influences

CULTURAL ISSUES IN MATHEMATICS EDUCATION

Multicultural and anti-racist issues in education, like those relating to gender, have received a lot of attention in recent years. They have not had the same kind of impact on the thinking of those concerned with mathematical education, however. Many teachers of mathematics remain unconvinced that multicultural considerations are of any real relevance in their subject: the view is sometimes expressed that of all disciplines mathematics is the most culture free. Mathematical structures are, after all, essentially abstract and have their own internal consistency, and so they do not depend on the culture and context in which they are taught and learned.

Unfortunately, the National Curriculum requirements encourage this view, by making no reference to racial and cultural differences. The consultation document on the National Curriculum proposals for mathematics (1988) included a short section entitled 'Ethnic and Cultural Diversity'. This section explains that:

> ...priority must be given to ensuring that they (the pupils) have the knowledge, understanding and skills which they will need for adult life and employment in Britain in the twenty-first century.

This, then, is the argument for not including any so-called multicultural topics in the attainment targets. The discussion is moderated a little in the following paragraph of the document, and then re-emphasised in the next, as if to suggest some imagined balance. It is emphasised that teachers need to devise examples and illustrations, within the National Curriculum framework, which relate to the cultural background of pupils. On the other hand, the idea that a multicultural approach is necessary to raise the self-esteem of minority cultures and improve mutual understanding and respect is rejected as misconceived and patronising. Finally, after a short consideration of problems with English language, the key principle is stated:

> ....attainment targets and programmes of study are the same for all pupils regardless of race.

There are, it seems, two ways of avoiding any racial or cultural concerns in mathematics education. The first is to assert the neutrality and abstractness of mathematics and argue that culture and context are not significant. The second, which is taken apparently by the National Curriculum, is to recognise the possibility of a multicultural approach but to decide for the most part not to adopt it: thus, school mathematics is to be directed firmly towards the 'mainstream' of British society.

The first approach, even if it could be implemented in practice, leads to an impossibly arid view of mathematics. It goes back to the comment made in one of the submissions to the Cockcroft Committee (1982):

> Mathematics lessons in secondary schools are very often not about anything. You collect like terms, or learn the laws of indices, with no perception of why anyone needs to do such things...
>
> As a consequence of this approach, school mathematics contains very little incidental information. A French lesson might well contain incidental information about France – so on across the curriculum; but in mathematics the incidental information which one might expect (current exchange and interest rates; general knowledge on climate, communications and geography; the rules and scoring systems of games; social statistics) is rarely there, because most teachers in no way see this as part of their responsibility when teaching mathematics.

The example quoted here makes it clear that whenever school mathematics is illustrated or applied in terms of the real and familiar world, it acquires a cultural context.

The second approach may prove to be equally unsatisfactory. If we recognise the possibility of an approach to teaching which takes account of ethnic and cultural diversity, but, apart from providing specially chosen illustrations to 'help' pupils from minority groups, we reject this route, what is likely to happen? Pupils will still learn about differences of race and culture at school, even if this is not a part of the official curriculum. Such learning is likely to become a part of the unintentional curriculum suggested in Chapter 7, and in this context it may be uncontrolled, garbled and quite probably racist.

In the recent literature of mathematics education, a lot of general agreement and common ground has been reached. This applies to much of the content of the curriculum, to matters such as the introduction of calculators and computers, and even, for example, to gender issues. There are unresolved arguments, but at least there is a basis on which these can be discussed. Debates about racism and multicultural education, however, appear to have no such basis. Apparently well-meaning people, with experience of teaching mathematics in multiracial communities, seem to have quite different perceptions of the issues. It is not so much that people are in conflict, but rather that they talk and write at cross purposes.

It may be helpful to distinguish amongst the various issues considered under the multicultural heading; obviously these are related, but they are also sufficiently distinct to merit separate definition. Five considerations can be identified.

- Mathematics is generally taught in a narrow context, with little concern for its historical and cultural setting. Would the subject be enriched by such concern?
- Is the mathematics curriculum in Britain racist, in the sense of discriminating against the needs, values and best interests of certain ethnic groups?
- To what extent can and should school mathematics be used politically, to promote certain values or social developments; and is it being used in this way?
- It is a common complaint that school mathematics is remote from the familiar experiences of many pupils. Could it usefully be more closely based on the pupils' 'culture', however that might be identified?
- Is studying the mathematics of a particular culture or society a reasonable and productive way of understanding that society?

MULTICULTURAL ENRICHMENT

Compared with many academic subjects, mathematics, in Britain in particular, has developed in a way which is almost divorced from any cultural context. It is possible to study mathematics at school and in higher education, and indeed to teach mathematics and become interested in the issues of mathematical education, with little or no knowledge of the origins and historical development of mathematics or of how it is taught and learned and used in other parts of the world. It is difficult to imagine a comparable situation in other fields: we should be surprised, for example, to find specialists in music or art with so little knowledge of the history of their subject and so little awareness of international and cross-cultural activity.

In the early 1980s especially, a number of books appeared which attempted to identify the problems and opportunities for the curriculum presented by a culturally diverse society. Most such books include a section on mathematics: a good example is the chapter by Hemmings (in Craft and Bardell, 1984). The theme of work of this kind is almost always the cultural broadening of classroom activity in mathematics. Hemmings claims that:

> there is an interesting diversity... which can considerably enrich the quality of mathematical activity in the classroom. This is understandably the first concern of a mathematics teacher; it is the intention of this Chapter to suggest some ways...

and so on. In itself, a greater concern for the culture and history of mathematics is a positive development. It can lead to a better understanding both of the structures of mathematics and of the contexts in which these structures can be learned and used. It broadens and enriches the intellectual demands of mathematics as a subject. But it is not necessarily a realistic response to the multiracial composition of the school population in Britain.

Woodrow (1984) has expressed a note of dissent on this matter in various articles and publications. His ideas about multicultural mathematics education have come in for some criticism, but he does recognise that those who are anxious to broaden the scope of the mathematics curriculum and those whose concern is to meet the needs of a multiracial population are not addressing the same issue. Multicultural enrichment seeks to rectify a perceived weakness in the discipline of mathematics. If this is a real weakness, and if the suggested new directions have genuine value in an academic, intellectual or practical sense, then the idea has to be given consideration. The merit of this argument, however, is not dependent on the client group, and it could presumably have been advanced regardless of any concern for multiracial policies.

Of course, a widening of the context of school mathematics may have beneficial spin-offs in racial terms. If symbols and words for numbers from other cultures and languages are discussed in mathematics lessons, this may enhance the self-esteem, participation and motivation of some children who are able to introduce and talk about these numbers. If pupils from various backgrounds can be encouraged to demonstrate games or geometrical designs, for example, which are a familiar part of their lives, then other children are given a better opportunity to understand these pupils and their culture. Yet, there are dangers in this as well. Sometimes the word 'tokenism' is used to disparage the introduction of topics merely because there are children from a different background in the class; Woodrow comments that 'to include Islamic art patterns simply because they are Islamic is to trivialise their value'. Similarly, references to the historical input of other civilisations in mathematics may serve to suggest that these are once great cultures which have somehow lost their excellence.

These considerations apart, there are a lot of insights to be derived from looking at the social and historical contexts in which mathematics is created and used. For the teacher, these insights can suggest new ways of presenting and working on topics. To some extent in schools, and to an even greater extent at higher levels, the education of mathematicians could be enhanced and humanised by such developments. Hemmings' chapter is a possible starting point, but there are plenty of other sources, many quoted in the Mathematical Association (1988) publication on *Mathematics in a Multicultural Society*.

For those wishing to extend their awareness of the historical and cultural context of numbers in particular, an excellent and very thorough source is provided by Menninger (1977). Flegg (1984) gives a very readable treatment of the history and meaning of numbers, which can generate a lot of useful classroom activities. There are plenty of books on the history of mathematics. For those who want to understand the historical and contemporary concerns of mathematicians, however, and to appreciate the context in which new and more advanced mathematical ideas are created, the best source is probably Davis and Hersh (1983).

RACISM AND ANTI-RACISM IN MATHEMATICS EDUCATION

Many of the features of mathematics education which ensure that girls are put at a disadvantage possess the same potential for discriminating against pupils from different ethnic and cultural backgrounds. By recognising how these influences operate, it should be possible at least to increase awareness of them and perhaps to begin to develop strategies for improvement.

Success in learning mathematics in schools relies heavily on earlier experiences and activities. Construction toys, practical work, familiarity with technology, and a variety of games are all accepted as useful in this respect. We know that girls are less likely to come with the benefit of this background, and yet relatively little attempt has been made to rethink the mathematics curriculum to make better use of girls' experiences. What we do is continue to operate in the same old way and try to persuade girls to adopt more of the interests and activities previously seen as 'male'. We really have no grounds for assuming that children from varied ethnic backgrounds will come to school with the benefit of those experiences which form a good basis for our present curriculum and style of teaching and learning. Most teachers would respond positively to the idea that they should value and build on the strengths which children bring with them to schools. In recognising the importance of this, Emblen (1988) also draws attention to the need for a greater awareness of what these strengths are.

On the whole, textbooks and other resources for teaching mathematics have been produced with little awareness of the dangers of reinforcing sexist and racist stereotypes. The situations used as examples, the people in texts and the roles they play, and the pictorial illustrations all contribute to this. Awareness of the problem is growing, but the message suggested by Jenner (1988) that 'only white boys participate in mathematics' is still implied by much material. Bias and insensitivity in educational resources can take many forms, and it is instructive to work through texts and schemes carefully just to see how unintentionally offensive some material can be. The ILEA booklet *Everyone Counts* (1985) is intended to help teachers identify such offensiveness in a range of categories. In the present context, material must be regarded as unacceptable if it:

- presents or appears to praise a narrow range of lifestyles;
- ignores or denigrates in some way certain groups of people;
- accepts and reinforces stereotypes;
- provides offensive visual images;
- shows ignorance of or lack of respect for religious, cultural and moral values.

Everyone Counts considers many other factors as well, but plenty of examples will be found of the range of prejudice quoted here. Indeed, it may well not be practical to discard material which is found unsatisfactory on these criteria, and teachers will be left using resources which they know exhibit bias. Sands (Mathematical Association 1988) suggests that in such a situation, whether the item is a book, computer program, workcard or whatever, teachers must react to show their awareness and dislike. Not to do so may be to give approval to the offensive message. There may even be cases where an apology for having to use the material is appropriate.

Just as teachers' expectations of girls and their interpretation of girls' interests and strengths may reinforce stereotypes, so teachers may learn to expect lower achievement from some groups. In education and employment in Britain, it is undeniable that black young people are on the whole underachieving. Jenner (1988) quotes a statement made in the 1960s by an enthusiastic teacher in an urban school:

> You have to remember that in a school such as ours the children are not as ready and willing to learn as in schools in middle-class neighbourhoods.

It is not difficult to find staff-rooms where similar views are stated – but now they are more likely to be held by teachers in schools which are not only urban but also multiracial in their intake. However much circumstances may appear to justify such attitudes, their acceptance as inevitable is unlikely to promote educational success.

One reason for girls' lack of motivation to participate in mathematics is the image of the subject as geared towards male ambitions. These ambitions are economic and technological – they are concerned with personal wealth, practical independence and a flourishing lifestyle in an advanced society. This is not simply a male domain: it is also the preserve of the fat cats – mostly the white middle classes. The assumption that such a vision is something to which all can aspire and contribute is far from justified. In the event, the promotion of competence in mathematics as a criterion for entry to power and success may well prove an effective way of preserving existing patterns of inequality.

The statutory requirements of the National Curriculum deliberately refrain from consideration of issues of gender and race. The consultative document (1988) elaborated on policy in relation to these issues. Although they are expressed in different forms, the approaches to gender and race are closely analogous. Targets have not been defined with girls (or boys) in mind: this means that considerations of gender bias have not been taken seriously. Similarly there are no multicultural considerations in the attainment targets: everyone must work towards the perceived norms of adult life and employment in Britain. We know that the school curriculum is such that girls underachieve and pupils from some ethnic groups underachieve, but we are not going to do anything about the curriculum. The message is that girls must change their interest and attitudes to become more like boys, and black people must change their interest and attitudes to become more like white people. In this sense, official policy in relation to the mathematics curriculum is inherently sexist and racist.

SOCIAL AND POLITICAL VALUES IN THE MATHEMATICS CURRICULUM

Whether or not such a view would be admitted by politicians, there is no doubt that the potential for using education to promote particular social values in Britain has become more exploited. Woodrow (1989) writes about Gerdes' work on changes in mathematics education in Mozambique, which is described as a 'less politically inhibited' society. In Mozambique, the tasks set in mathematics lessons have changed with the political climate, so that at one stage problems involving differential pay scales for men and women or the relationship between landlord and tenant, for example, became unacceptable. At the same time, it was quite acceptable to introduce questions which mentioned 'guerilla fighters'. Woodrow's view is that the inclusion of such explicitly political, value-laden concepts is less acceptable in the British context and would be labelled as 'indoctrination'.

Woodrow himself, however, in earlier articles, has quoted examples which could be seen as promoting social change – problems about filling baths, for example, which were set to pupils most of whom had no experience of baths at home. He mentioned too the inclusion of questions on stocks and shares, again attempted by pupils whose home environment was most unlikely to advocate such investments. Grugnetti's (1979) work on health promotion through the mathematics curriculum in Sardinia is frequently quoted, and yet there is a very comparable British example to be found in the unit on 'Smoking and Health' in the Schools Council Project on Statistical Education.

In practice, like it or not, the education system has become part of the political arena. The directing of mathematical education towards economic activity is indicated by the words 'for adult life *and employment*' already quoted. Courses of teacher training are now required to educate students for 'economic awareness', and links between education and industry are emphasised and commended. The view is suggested by politicians that sociologists have introduced an anti-industry bias into teacher education and that this must be rectified. All these are overtly political manipulations of education.

The insistence that imperial measures remain a part of school mathematics may be a reflection of everyday life, but it is still a political gesture. Some multicultural themes, including apparently innocent topics such as different number systems or foreign currencies, are discouraged because they 'could confuse young children'. Such matters do not seem very different from comparing two sets of measures, but perhaps educational arguments have to be modified to suit the political implications of each issue.

The Mathematical Association (1988) booklet includes some work by Zanetti on using statistics and percentages to look at racial discrimination: as an activity for the mathematics lesson, this would in earlier years have been of doubtful acceptability. Yet, Woodrow remains tentative about suggesting a project on uneconomic coalmines. It seems to have rich opportunities for mathematics: the whole idea of what 'uneconomic' means in this context opens the way to a whole variety of mathematical models.

It would be idle to pretend now that mathematical education does not convey messages about social and political values. To an extent, it always did. We have experienced not so much a loss of innocence as a coming out into the open: subtle and clandestine pressure has been replaced by more explicit, political issues. At least, in this climate, it is more obvious what is happening.

THE CULTURE OF PUPILS

A recurrent theme in discussions of cultural issues in mathematics education is the view that, if children are to achieve their potential, we must recognise, take account of and build upon the strengths and experience which they already have. In many schools, pupils have a great deal in common with one another, and will recognise familiar experiences in talking together about their lives outside school. They will also, of course, share a lot of activity and experience outside their formal education. In other schools, children have more diverse home and cultural backgrounds; here, we hope to enable all pupils to become aware of, understand and respond positively to this diversity.

Alongside this diversity, however, there is another disparity. This is the gap between the pupils' culture – their interests, activities and values – and the culture of their teachers, their school, and especially their mathematics lessons. Jenner offers the suggestion that the materials used in mathematics need to provide 'images of a world which pupils recognise and feel part of, not unrealistic, ill-informed views of their pupils' cultures'. The context for her comments is a multicultural one and her concern is that teachers might expect, for example, Islamic patterns to be familiar to, and have meaning for, all Moslem children. Yet the remark is applicable to all kinds of situations where the teacher's view of what are real and relevant illustrations of mathematical ideas is not shared by the pupils.

The notion of relevance is explored in an article by Edmonds and Ball (1988). Relevance is a popular idea in education. It is something which almost all will agree is worth striving for, and yet pupils, teachers, parents, politicians and any other group with an interest in the process of education will express different ideas of what kind of learning is relevant. Perhaps this is especially true of learning mathematics.

One of the consequences of disagreement about what is relevant is that so-called 'real life' problems presented in mathematics lessons are not part of pupils' real life at all. They are advocated as useful for some future kind of employment, or as necessary for such everyday activities as checking the telephone bill, or just used to dress up an activity or investigation in more picturesque terms. There may be justification for all these things, but they are not ways of making use of the world of the pupils.

Several writers, in asking how situations and activities can be found in which mathematics can develop and which are part of the lives and interests of pupils, have come to the same conclusion. They must come from the pupils themselves. In writing about mathematical modelling in schools, Burkhardt (1981) makes the following suggestion for finding suitable problems for modelling: 'ask the pupils'. Edmonds and Ball, discussing projects for GCSE coursework, maintain that the value of projects lies 'less in the subject matter than in the fact that topics are chosen and worked upon by the pupils themselves'.

If you are responsible for teaching mathematics to a class of children, ask yourself these questions:

- Do the children play games of their own free will and in their leisure time, which involve mathematical thinking and have a mathematical structure?
- Do they handle money, carry out calculations with money or deal with any complicated financial transactions?
- Do they ever produce models, designs or patterns for any purpose, whether using paper or card or cloth?
- When, why and how do they use calculators or microcomputers outside school?
- Have they any interest at all in puzzles?

It seems unlikely that most teachers have any clear idea of their pupils' mathematical culture. Doubtless you could invent more questions – better questions. But you could still miss that one aspect of a pupil's life which is most important, and potentially richest in mathematical development.

The December 1986 issue of *Mathematics Teaching* is a special edition concerned with the roots of mathematical activity. In it, many people describe experiences which they recognise as significant, either in developing their mathematical thinking or in motivating them towards mathematics. Inevitably, because of the nature of the publication, these are mostly people who have become more committed than most to the study of mathematics. The situations described are appealing and enormously varied, but some things are very clear. None of the contributors seems to have been motivated by persuasion about future employment needs, and there is nothing remotely like the need to check a telephone bill.

MATHEMATICS AND UNDERSTANDING SOCIETY

If we wanted to gain some insight into the workings of an unfamiliar social or cultural group – a small nation in today's Africa perhaps, or a historical civilisation such as the Mayas, or even a large, industrial, modern power like Japan, there are many features on which we might focus. It all depends on our particular interest. We could concentrate on some social institution such as education, religion or family life, perhaps comparing it with our own experience in Britain. If our particular interest were in art or music or literature or fashion, we might well analyse this aspect, and try to understand the different society in our own terms.

But let's say that our specialist interest is in mathematics. We observe the workings of a community in these terms. We try to identify what mathematics people do and how they do it. We look at money transactions and how people handle them, at the currency and the coinage. We look at the words and symbols for numbers, at how people do arithmetic and at what calculating aids they use. We consider the measurement of time, and how people talk about time, and what importance it has for them. We look at pattern, design, shape and geometrical construction in all aspects of community life. We ask about games, learn how to play them, and tease out the mathematical elements. All these things we might do and more, and especially we should ask people what mathematics they think is important in their lives and why. If there is a high culture of mathematics in this community, with research in university mathematics departments perhaps, or people employed in commerce or industry for their specialist mathematical skills, we look at this too.

Is this a good, productive, informative way of understanding a society? Well, it ought at least to identify features central to the workings of the society. Literature or music could prove to be peripheral: indeed they might be ways in which people looked for 'escape' from the realities of their lives. Mathematics is rather more likely to be considered intrinsic to this particular piece of civilisation.

It is hard to point to anything resembling a study of this kind. Academic work has not taken this particular direction: research on mathematics as a social institution is, to say the least, thin on the ground. Perhaps the nearest analysis is that provided by Zaslavsky (1973) in her descriptions of various aspects of mathematical activity in some parts of Africa.

Those who have studied the history of Africa during the twentieth century, and particularly those with an interest in education, sometimes write about the 'inappropriate education' system, especially in times of colonial administration. Indeed, in reading Zaslavsky's work, it is very difficult to reconcile her description of the mathematics of daily life with some of the textbooks which were produced for use in schools in the same part of Africa at that time. These are commonly found to be barely disguised rewrites of familiar European series, with only the names and places changed. These cosmetic changes did little to make the schemes relevant to African life.

We might take a little comfort from our confidence that in Britain today the mathematics curriculum is not entirely unaware of the experience, needs and aspirations of the population. Yet the purpose of this chapter is perhaps to indicate that the match is not as close as we might imagine. It raises, too, some awkward questions about who 'owns' the mathematics curriculum, who should have the right to decide what is appropriate, and on what grounds.

In looking again at Gerdes' work, Woodrow (1989) sees some resemblance between the African experience and developments in Britain. Mathematics learning in parts of Africa has changed from 'folk' or tribal learning, through a period of colonial education, to what is termed 'democratic' mathematics. In Britain, from the clerical arithmetic of Victorian schooling, through the 'industrial' mathematics of the first part of the twentieth century, we have reached a new stage which Woodrow describes as the 'mathematics of understanding and processes'. He wrote this just before the appearance of the National Curriculum, however, and it is a little hard to see how the National Curriculum fits into this model.

There is one more point in Woodrow's discussion which is worth picking up. He comments that 'remnants of previous ages always remain'. This recalls to mind the requirement of the number attainment which was mentioned in Chapter 2 as having an almost ritualistic aspect:

> (using whole numbers) understand and use non-calculator methods by which a three-digit number is multiplied by a two-digit number and a three-digit number is divided by a two-digit number.

Here is a new explanation for its inclusion. It is not so much that it is interesting or useful – it is just a remnant of a previous age, and, so far at least, too cherished to discard. After the Russian revolution, the communist authorities set about creating procedures for the normal rites of daily life, marriages and funerals and what have you. Some aspects were retained, even though their religious and cultural significance did not fit logically alongside the new ideas. In the National Curriculum, pupils should 'make use of *appropriate* methods of calculation', and the illustrations clearly indicate that 'appropriateness' may well mean using a calculator. Yet we still have the requirement quoted above. This is *syncretism* in the National Curriculum.

Chapter 17

Language and mathematics education

SOME COMPARISONS BETWEEN MATHEMATICS AND LANGUAGE

Language plays a significant role in all kinds of learning and it is not surprising that success in mathematics depends on language factors in a variety of ways. It is common, however, to read statements which point to a still closer relationship: many writers express the view that mathematics is itself a language. Some find this unhelpful: Austin and Howson (1979), for example, and Bell *et al.* (1983) are anxious to contradict the view. Yet its frequent repetition suggests that many people have found the idea valuable, and this justifies the attempt to explore its interpretation.

Clearly, mathematics is not a language in the sense in which Urdu, say, or Welsh is. Two people from different countries whose only common knowledge was mathematics could not use this language to transact the ordinary business of daily life, as they could if they were both fluent in German for example. If we take this intuitive view of the normal, literal meaning of the word 'language', then it does not apply to mathematics. In describing mathematics as a language we are either accepting a broader meaning of the world or – more reasonably perhaps – the statement is metaphorical.

Two somewhat different interpretations are possible. One is that mathematics is called a language in the sense that we might say that music is a language, or art is a language, or even clothes are a language. By such means, we are able to convey to other people particular ideas or feelings or perspectives, which are not easily expressed in ordinary words. This is an attractive notion of mathematics, as a vehicle for communication of patterns, relationships, structures and properties which cannot effectively be described in any other way. The Cockcroft Report (1982) takes up this theme, suggesting that mathematics is useful because it provides a means of communication which is powerful, concise and unambiguous.

A second interpretation, however, although superficially reasonable, leads to a narrow and misleading view of what mathematics is about. Describing mathematics as a 'language' may bring to mind the large collection of special words and symbols associated with the subject: +, =, π, histogram, equation, cross-multiply, cancel and so on. It is important to recognise that this collection of words and symbols is not in itself mathematics – any more than the words and symbols in which music is written or described are themselves music. Mathematics is an activity and a body of knowledge, which is normally denoted and enacted in terms of a fairly standardised language. A completely different set of words and notation could be used; and, in reality, mathematical terminology is not nearly so standardised and unambiguous as many people imagine or would like to claim.

Explained in this way, the two interpretations of mathematics as a language are recognisably different, but the distinction is easily blurred. Suppose we consider school algebra. As discussed in Chapter 3, a credible justification for introducing algebra is its power to express relationships in a clear and concise form. In defining the 'triangular numbers', for example, as sums of natural numbers, we might write:

$$\begin{aligned} T_1 &= 1 \\ T_2 &= 1+2 \\ T_3 &= 1+2+3 \\ &\dots \\ T_n &= 1+2+3+\dots+n \end{aligned}$$

Then, using the arguments of Chapter 3, we obtain a short-cut way of calculating T_n which is written as a formula:

$$T_n = \frac{1}{2}n(n+1)$$

Now, although all this exploration is possible without the use of algebra, the algebraic notation allows the relationships to be expressed in a clearer and more accessible way.

Unfortunately, learning the 'language' of algebra can sometimes degenerate into learning its notation and conventions without using these to express any understood structure or relationhip. In one sense, this is typified by the use of questions like:

Add 4 on to $3n$

In trying to push the analogy between language and algebraic notation, Pimm (1987) compares examples of over-generalised transformations. Thus, a child who says 'I goed' rather than 'I went' is over-using the rule which constructs the past tense by adding '-ed'. Similarly, a mistake such as

$$(A+B)^2 = A^2 + B^2$$

is an over-extension of the distributive law, which might even be legitimised by the remark, 'you have to square everything in the bracket'.

The resemblance between these two situations, however, is superficial. In the use of the expression 'goed', the meaning is quite clear, and the message which the child wants to communicate is readily interpretable. In contrast, writing $(A+B)^2$ as $A^2 + B^2$ indicates the absence of any message or interpretation. The mistake is a likely one, because the activity is being pursued as a meaningless game, with rules which can appear to lack consistency.

In this context, Pimm argues that language teaching has moved away from the explicit teaching of rules, for constructing the past tense or the plural for example. Rather, language is taught in the context of its usage, and it would indeed seem strange to carry out syntactical operations on words or phrases without a clear awareness of their meaning or purpose. Yet algebra is frequently taught in this way, with an emphasis on operations on symbols. This is not done thoughtlessly: indeed a conscious and deliberate decision may be made to tell pupils, for example, to:

- do the same thing to both sides;
- collect together the *x*s;
- multiply out the brackets.

Sometimes, language and meaning are sufficiently separable for success or failure to be allocated to one category or the other. Thus, 'I goed' shows no difficulty with meaning but is an incorrect use of language, whereas expressing $(A+B)^2$ as $A^2 + B^2$ seems to show failure in both understanding and symbol operation. It is of course possible to manipulate the symbols correctly to give

$$(A + B)^2 = A^2 + 2AB + B^2$$

without any awareness of the meaning or purpose of this activity. There are comparable examples in language: you might, for instance, if asked for the plural of the word 'agneau', correctly guess 'agneaux', without attaching any meaning to this.

There are no doubt situations in learning mathematics where 'failure' is attributable not to lack of understanding of the mathematics but to an inability to communicate this understanding in appropriate words and symbols. The nature of this failure may not be readily identifiable. An example is quoted in Passages (*Mathematics Teaching* 1987) of a child being taken on a car journey and asking a series of questions, beginning:

'Are we nearly there yet?'

The next question was:

'Are we half way there?'

The answer 'no' produced the question:

'Are we a quarter of the way there?'

The reply was:

'We are *more* than a quarter of the way'.

At this stage the desire to elicit a more precise description of the relative distance provoked some quiet thought. You can imagine the child thinking of the journey divided into quarters, concentrating on the interval between a quarter and a half, even visualising the mid-point of this interval, and yet still not having sufficient command of the language of fractions to ask the appropriate question. Eventually, the question came:

'Are we three thirds of the way there?'

It is not complete nonsense. After all, we have 'halves, quarters, thirds...'; a third could mean a third 'cut', couldn't it? Perhaps this is more closely analogous to Pimm's 'I goed' than the algebraic example: the intended meaning was understood in the context, but the language was used in a spectacularly incorrect way. Yet, here, the distinction between meaning and language has become blurred. Is this a child who does not understand fractions – or who does not know the proper language to describe them? And how separable are these?

To describe mathematics as a means of communication is misleading if it suggests that mathematics cannot be a solitary activity. Certainly 'doing' mathematics does not have to involve telling it to another person: some might say that a desert island would be an ideal place to do mathematics. Even in a utilitarian sense, we might use mathematics purely for our own benefit with no intention of letting other people see it – we could, for example, write down a calculation on a bank statement to bring it up to date, or make a plan of a room or a plot of land, put measurements on it and sketch out ideas. In these situations, our mathematical activity allows us to reflect on the problem at the time and keep a record for future reference. There are plenty of comparable occasions when ordinary language is used in this way: the suggested use of lesson plans and diary notes in Chapter 8 of this book is an obvious example.

It has to be admitted that one function of mathematical notation is to make manipulative operations and calculations easier. If a complicated situation can be reduced to a set of equations or to a neatly laid out set of figures and calculations, it may become much more tractable. Furthermore, by setting down the problem in this way, we may be able to work on a small part of it at a time, without having to keep the whole context and meaning constantly in mind. This represents a considerable reduction in the cognitive strain required. In such circumstances, competent mathematicians may well forget about the context and meaning for a while, and operate solely on the formal structure provided by the symbols. This operational fluency, however, is very much on the surface: it hides the real competence, which lies in the ability to reinterpret and check the results of the mathematical operations, at any stage, in the context of the problem under consideration.

Because operational fluency is often an overt manifestation of mathematical understanding, such fluency may be mistakenly identified as the essence of mathematical competence. Indeed, it sometimes seems as if a lot of teaching is directed only towards fluency with the symbols – as though the strategy is to ensure that pupils appear to behave like competent mathematicians, even if they lack any understanding. There is perhaps another parallel with language ability here: pupils whose education has emphasised precise and articulate use of language and who have developed a wide vocabulary may well be able to give an overly favourable impression of their general intellectual competence. On the other hand, a well-developed language fluency can be an aid to logical thinking. Much of our ability to think through ideas and arguments and possible courses of action depends on our capacity to put these matters into words – even if the words are not spoken aloud. In this respect, ordinary language shares something of the manipulative function of mathematical symbolism.

One aspect of mathematical activity which should not be neglected in this discussion is the intrinsic pleasure which it can provide. Playing with numbers, investigating their properties and relationships, constructing shapes and geometrical models, finding neat arguments to justify generalisations – these are all areas of mathematics in which people find considerable satisfaction. This satisfaction can be enjoyed without necessarily sharing it with others and regardless of whether the work has any utilitarian value or not. Again, a comparison with language is possible. Those who write, especially poetry but also short stories – perhaps even diaries and letters sometimes – may do so, not to communicate with others nor even so much to record their thoughts, but rather for the inherent satisfaction of organising ideas and words in this way.

TALKING

Much traditional mathematics teaching is about talking. It involves the teacher expounding a mathematical topic, questioning pupils and eliciting verbal responses, and checking by talking either to the class or individual pupils how much they do or do not understand. When mathematics teaching is based on an individualised learning scheme, teachers have little opportunity to talk to and with the whole class, except maybe about organisational matters such as when and how to tidy up and leave the room. Instead, teachers talk with individual pupils, prompting them, offering help and advice, or listening and making encouraging suggestions. In such lessons, talk amongst pupils is likely to be peripheral to the mathematical activity: promoting differences in topic, level and pace does not make co-operative learning particularly feasible.

Given this scenario, it is hardly surprising that conversation and discussion amongst pupils in mathematics lessons have not become regarded as legitimate or valuable very quickly. The classroom styles most commonly adopted in mathematics do not readily accommodate such talk, nor do they appear to promote any improvement in pupils' speaking or listening skills. Indeed, an informal survey of mathematics classrooms visited during the course of development of APU materials revealed that almost no work of this type was being done intentionally (Joffe and Foxman 1989).

Pimm (1987) uses an interesting expression when he describes the strategy of encouraging discussion and conversation between pupils as a 'gambit'. The word suggests a belief that this move will lead in the longer term to more successful teaching and learning, but that it demands some immediate sacrifice on the part of the teacher. The sacrifice is a loss of control. The talk in the classroom is no longer prescribed by the teacher: it may take different directions and lead to unpredicted developments. Furthermore, chatter in the classroom is still regarded by some as weak discipline, and even recent surveys of discipline in schools have identified 'talking in class' as the commonest form of disruptive behaviour on the part of pupils.

For some, it may be quite an effort to see discussion and co-operation as a positive, enriching aspect of learning mathematics. Permission for pupils to work together may even be given as a somewhat reluctant concession: 'You can talk – quietly – provided you are talking about the work'. Discussion is seen as a privilege rather than a technique to be developed, encouraged and exploited.

Plenty of descriptions of children's talk in mathematics lessons are available (see, for example, Smith 1987, Pirie and Schwarzenberger 1988). Such work encourages the view that interpersonal communication skills can be developed in the mathematics classroom, and that these skills can be used in a purposeful way, so that pupils develop and refine their own ideas and help one another to learn. It is in group work on mathematical investigations that pupils' talk finds its most obvious role, and various attempts have been made to classify this talk. It may be possible, for example, to distinguish:

- genuine mathematical discussion, in which pupils ask and answer questions of one another, explain their answers or strategies, suggest possible approaches, and negotiate thoughts and ideas;
- thinking aloud, which is not genuinely co-operative, may or may not be valuable to other members of the group, and may serve to summarise or even slow down the work;
- spontaneous verbalisation, an expression of a sudden insight, not essentially interactive and not always meaningful to the rest of the group, which requires subsequent explanation and articulation.

Other categories are possible. So far, these are concerned directly with the mathematical work, but all writers in this area agree that non-mathematical talk of an emotional, political, social or incidental nature always arises. Pupils seem to need to express their affective response to the work, to establish roles and relationships within the group, and to intersperse the discussion with social remarks. Pirie and Schwarzenberger quote: 'Where are you going on holiday at Easter?', 'My guinea-pig has had babies'.... Such interjections do not necessarily distract pupils from the flow of the work: indeed they may be a necessary element in enabling many pupils to sustain mathematical discussion. The insistence that talk may continue only if it is about the mathematics may be either counter-productive or unenforceable.

There is some evidence to support the plausible view that discussion and conversation are more likely to drift away from the task in hand when this task is not well matched to the ability of those working on it. People who carry out routine work, which demands and holds only a part of their attention, are inclined to alleviate the lack of intellectual stimulation by talking – and not about the work. This is familiar in industry and in domestic life, and it happens in classrooms. It can lead to a situation where the work and talk go on in a parallel, unrelated way. On the other hand, discussion can sometimes be used as a delaying tactic, to avoid starting on a task which is too difficult or not well understood and which appears insurmountable.

These considerations suggest that purposeful, directed discussion needs a context whose cognitive demand matches the ability level of the pupils, and, in a broad sense, this is probably true. It would obviously be stupid to present pupils with a diet of unremittingly trivial routine work, or to set tasks on which they had little hope of ever succeeding, and expect to hear any useful mathematical discussion. But precise matching may not be a sensible aim. For one thing, work on investigations in particular can allow pupils to set the level of cognitive demand for themselves, by adopting a more or less sophisticated approach. Also (and more significantly) the demands of life are not consistently matched to ability. We are sometimes called upon to carry out undemanding routine work, and sometimes meet situations which we feel unable to handle. In the event, we find strategies for coping – and co-operation, conversation and discussion form part of these strategies. In this respect, mathematics is not especially different from any other human activity, and the idea that it should always be very finely tuned to the precise level of pupils' understanding, however laudable, is largely unrealistic.

Part of the reason for encouraging pupils to talk about mathematics and to negotiate mathematical ideas for themselves lies in the growth in popularity of a constructivist view of learning mathematics. In this context, the notion that children are capable of constructing their own knowledge of mathematics in their own unique ways (see Ernest 1989) is acceptable to most teachers; more contentious is the claim that this is the *only* way of acquiring mathematical knowledge. It is clear, however, that children can only learn for themselves: teachers, parents and anyone else involved cannot do the learning for them, and no amount of telling children something, in any number of predigested and regurgitated forms, will guarantee that they will learn it. This perspective gives some credence to the view that effective learning may be better promoted by giving pupils some opportunity to negotiate their own understanding through talking.

Becoming an effective mathematics teacher requires the development of a range of personal skills. A naive suggestion might be that one fundamental skill is the ability to go into a classroom and talk, in a way that holds the attention of pupils and makes them listen. Such is the culture of schools that this will no doubt always be considered important. A stereotyped teacher's remark is: 'Listen, and you might learn something'. Sometimes, in mathematics teaching, this is more a statement of pious hope than a realistic promise. The implication of this section is that it may be at least as valuable for pupils to learn to talk in mathematics lessons – to negotiate, construct and articulate their own understanding of mathematics. Perhaps, then, teachers will be able to listen – and to recognise and accept pupils' understanding of mathematics in the pupils' terms.

READING

For a number of years, changes in the style of mathematics lessons have required an increase in the demands on pupils to read. Textbooks, worksheets and so on, once used almost exclusively as sources of exercises on taught work, now provide material from which pupils are expected to learn new ideas. Individualised schemes are designed to introduce topics through the material rather than relying on teacher exposition. These trends have led to an increased concern about the readability of mathematical text. Shuard and Rothery (1984) provide a detailed discussion of the issues involved, and a whole range of suggestions for teachers, textbook writers and those interested in further research in this area.

Many readability formulae have been devised to compare the readability of text: such formulae involve counting or measuring some aspects of the text and are usually based on the study of continuous prose. There is little evidence that these formulae can be of use in analysing mathematical text. The features which such formulae highlight, however, such as the length of words and length of sentences do have some influence on the accessibility of the material to pupils. For this reason, some have suggested that every effort should be made to 'improve' mathematical text by reducing such difficulties. This might mean the following:

- Using short sentences.
- Using simple words.
- Removing unnecessary descriptive material.
- Avoiding complicated sentence structures.

On the other hand, this downgrading of language can produce text which is considered unsatisfactory for other reasons: a compromise approach is needed.

Most mathematical activity is introduced to pupils in a form which involves rather more than words and sentences. There may be pictures, diagrams, tables, equations and lots of other devices – and the layout and presentation can have a significant effect on the usefulness of the material. Increasingly, pupils are used to professional presentation techniques, and there is some evidence to suggest that most prefer typewritten rather than handwritten material. Technological developments, such as the increasing availability of desk-top publishing facilities, make good presentation more accessible, but they are also likely to make pupils less tolerant of casually produced material.

One problem associated with learning from texts or schemes is that pupils are disinclined to regard these as reading material: they look for something to do. An SMP booklet or a KMP card is not something you read – it is something you do. With this attitude in mind, pupils skim quickly through the expository text, looking for the question. As a way of compensating for this, the authors of schemes have tended to keep the introductory material short, or to intersperse short sections of exposition between questions. This approach is not always helpful, and it can even alienate some pupils who find it difficult to identify what they are expected to do within the text.

In many situations, it appears that pupils could be helped more to use the scheme to better advantage. It needs to be emphasised that the booklets or workcards or whatever are not there just to provide work for pupils, but for pupils to learn new ideas from them as well. Their purpose is to develop some mathematical thinking and then involve the reader in some mathematical activity. Inevitably, the success of such text will be limited because it cannot interact with the reader; but the distinctive role of the teacher, in an individualised learning system in particular, is to enable pupils to use the text in a questioning, active and flexible way.

WRITING

The growing demands on pupils' linguistic skills in mathematics lessons take a variety of forms. Not only are pupils expected to listen, to talk and to read, they may also be expected to write about their work in mathematics. The tradition that mathematics involves established methods and standard ways of setting work out lingers on, as does the view that mistakes, crossings out and abortive first attempts at a problem are not acceptable. On the other hand, over the years, the fashion for emphasising process aspects of mathematics, and some more open-ended approaches to GCSE coursework, have encouraged greater freedom in the recording of mathematical work.

In secondary schools, and especially in the 14–16 age range, pupils spend a lot of time writing. For many this will probably be the only time in their lives when they write very much. Furthermore, the experience of coursework demands in the early years of GCSE suggests that the production of a substantial amount of written work is a considerable burden for a lot of pupils. For these reasons, it is worth stopping to think about it, rather than demanding automatically that when children do mathematics they should write it down, or, to use a subtle change of phrase, 'write it up'.

There are lots of different occasions in mathematics lessons when teachers feel it important for pupils to record something. In formal class teaching, it is common to go through an example on the board and instruct pupils to copy down the example. The argument for this is likely to be that the example is there to be imitated as a model answer for the exercises which follow – and for future reference. In some cases, brief notes may be given to accompany the example, either copied from the board or even in dictated form. As a device for learning mathematics, copying down a model example is not particularly effective, and it is hard to imagine a situation in school mathematics where it makes much sense to dictate notes. Nevertheless, given the style of teaching, some rationalisation can be provided for requiring pupils to write the work down.

When pupils work on exercises in mathematics, they are commonly subjected to a variety of requirements to document or annotate their work in particular ways. Teachers may say the following:

- Don't just put the answer ....
- Show your working ....
- Set it out in this way ....

If justification is required, it may be:

- When I mark this, I need to see where and how pupils have 'gone wrong'... a wrong answer alone is not helpful... the 'mistake' will be found in the method....
- In an examination, even if the answer is wrong, there may be some marks for the method....

Again, these are understandable concerns, but the approach has its disadvantages. Most worryingly, pupils who are well able to complete the tasks successfully by some logical procedure of their own may be constrained to write the answer in some different – and for them quite artificial – format, just to satisfy the teacher.

The demands for writing described so far can be justified in particular ways. There are plenty of grounds for doubt and criticism, but there are at least some articulated reasons for the requirements, which can provide a basis for discussion. The kind of writing which attracts most interest, however – and most enthusiasm – is quite different. It arises from pupils' activities or investigations, which are written up in a descriptive form. It is commonly considered worthwhile that such writing should include not only the mathematical structures and relationships discovered but also a description of the process of thinking, exploring and discussing which led to this discovery. Aspects of this process are regarded as important learning objectives – framing suitable questions, devising strategies which might lead to a solution, and recognising patterns are all significant features to be identified in the writing.

Of course, pupils working on a mathematical activity may be involved in these processes, whether or not they write about them. The writing provides the evidence. It is useful for teachers (who become aware of their pupils' thinking), to examiners (who may be able to assess an extended range of objectives) and to writers and researchers (who like to analyse examples of pupils' work). It is also to some extent useful to pupils – but not all the time: constant demands for written reports can become a laborious and time-consuming imposition.

There are lots of mathematical activities which pupils can undertake in the classroom without writing. There are games and puzzles which can be played, discussed and analysed using a variety of equipment and materials. Computer facilities, such as LOGO and NUMERATOR, can provide a framework for developing sophisticated mathematical structures. Geometrical ideas can be developed through projects involving the construction of models. The results of computer work can often be printed out, and geometrical construction work has its own finished product. It is not essential to 'write up' any of these activities. Recent issues of journals include a lot of examples of pupils' written work in these areas – these are helpful in showing how classroom activity has developed. The work is also often recognisably good: pupils' writing about their mathematics can be creative, amusing and full of insight. It is clear that this work has a useful place in secondary mathematics, although an over-insistence on writing up everything would be ill-advised.

MATHEMATICAL TERMINOLOGY

Most of the words used in mathematics, especially at secondary school level, are not exclusive to the subject. Admittedly, there are a few words – including, perhaps, 'parallelogram' and 'ratio' – which you would not expect to meet outside the mathematics classroom, but on the whole mathematics shares words with the real world. Of course, the words have a different meaning in mathematics. Some examples are:

- volume
- area
- origin
- co-ordinate
- difference
- product
- bracket
- index
- power

In everyday life, 'volume' refers to the loudness of a television, radio or music system, and 'area' is used in a variety of contexts with some interesting regional variations. 'Difference' and 'product' are especially nonsensical words in mathematics – prizes could be offered for the most creative answers to a question such as:

What is the difference between 4 and 5?

There are words in mathematics, too, which have different but related meanings depending on the context: 'square' refers to a geometrical shape and to a particular kind of number. There are words which many mathematics teachers would like to regard as precisely defined but which texts use loosely – 'histogram' and 'equation' are examples. It is even possible to find texts which define the prime numbers to include 1: no doubt there is an argument for this decision, but it does not make for unique factorisation.

Perhaps the most erratically used words are prepositions. We might read a division as '6 *into* 258':

$$6\overline{)258}$$

Then the multiplication of a bracket is 'x *into* $(2x + 3)$':

$$x\,(2x + 3)$$

We add 4 *to* 5, subtract 4 *from* 5, multiply 4 *by* 5, and yet consider the difference between 4 *and* 5. As cues, these words are often unhelpful: 'by', for example, can indicate multiplication or division depending on the context.

The words are intended to communicate mathematical structures and relationships, yet the concern must be that they can act as barriers to the recognition of the mathematical ideas. Some evidence that this happens is provided in a series of articles by Nicholson (1977, 1980, 1989) – one question quoted in the 1977 article is:

Give one example of a multiple of 30.

Only 21 out of 185 pupils tested gave a correct answer. Most of the others gave a factor rather than a multiple – many gave an example of a factorisation such as '5 x 6' or '10 x 3'. It is clear that these children understand the numerical properties and relationships – they simply do not know what 'multiple' means.

The APU surveys confirm this: the item in Chapter 4 about the area of a T-shape is a good example. If the word 'area' is replaced by an explanatory phrase such as 'number of 1 cm squares to cover the shape', very many more pupils can produce a correct answer. The word 'area' does not evoke the idea.

The implications of this work are twofold. One is that the specialist vocabulary of school mathematics should be examined to decide whether all these words are genuinely helpful or necessary: no doubt there are some whose usage could be abandoned. Second, having decided which words are important, we need to recognise that a word itself may be an impediment to pupils' awareness of the idea behind it. This may mean that some teaching should be aimed explicitly at knowing what words mean.

LEARNING MATHEMATICS IN A SECOND LANGUAGE

Over the years, various views have been expressed about the effect of bilingual upbringing, or a change in language through migration, on children's mathematical development. Early studies in this field are surveyed by Austin and Howson (1979); they suggest that, on the whole, genuine bilingualism may well be an advantage, and that there is no great disadvantage (other circumstances being favourable) in starting to learn mathematics in a second language. Indeed, some early writers suggested that the greatest danger was of frustrating such children by presenting them with undemanding work in mathematics if linguistic difficulties masked their real level of achievement in the subject.

In this respect, however, circumstances and opinions are changing. For one thing, ordinary language competence has come to play a somewhat greater part in mathematics lessons. Reading, talking and writing are important features of school mathematics, so that weak speakers of English find greater difficulty in taking part, and need support.

Also, there is a greater awareness of the more subtle linguistic aspects of mathematics which create difficulties. Of course some mathematical notation is relatively independent of the language of its context. An expression such as $x^2 - 6x + 9$ may be read aloud in English or a variety of other languages – it is equally intelligible in Germany or Japan for example. Also, some forms of mathematical 'problem' are so stereotyped that they are easily recognisable in any language. Glenn (1986) quotes the following Norwegian example:

> En mann kjøpte en traktor for 4875 kr og en moped for 1960 kr.
> Hva betalte han til sammen?

It is instructive to try to read some mathematics in a language of which your knowledge is weak, with the aid of a dictionary if necessary. Equations and symbolism are not a great problem, nor is technical terminology. The real difficulty is in appreciating the nuances of meaning conveyed by different prepositions and connectives. In Greek text, for example, the word 'απο' might appear amongst a string of algebraic equations. The dictionary may tell you this means 'at, by, for, from, with, ...', and in this context it is obviously intended to indicate the logical relationship between two lines of the argument – but its exact significance is elusive. English mathematics is full of details like this: words like 'any' and 'let' create problems for lots of pupils, but may be quite inaccessible to those whose experience of English is limited.

Some research quoted in the early 1980s (Zepp 1981, 1982; Jones 1982) concentrated on logical connectives and on comparative forms: these are areas of particular difficulty because they may not have any real parallels in some languages. These studies report certain detailed aspects of pupils' difficulties which are not resolved until the pupils concerned acquire command of relevant linguistic forms in English. Interestingly, some of these pupils remain unable to reproduce these expressions of mathematical relationships in their first language.

It must be said, however, that these are isolated examples. For the most part, children whose first language is not English may well understand and use concepts which they cannot yet express in English. Emblen (1988) recognises this in drawing attention to the importance of accepting the meaning and intention of a communication, without criticising the form it takes. Children unfamiliar with English will inevitably use more non-verbal means of communication than other pupils in English schools and they are likely to need more time to devise ways of expressing their ideas.

In practical terms, Emblen provides probably the most useful advice available about the problems and implications of learning mathematics in a second language. There do not appear to be any special practices or techniques which teachers must acquire to work with bilingual children in mathematics. Rather, like all pupils, such children are likely to benefit from the opportunity to construct and formulate mathematical ideas in their own terms and in familiar language.

SUMMARY

The relationship between language and mathematics education is a common enough theme in books and articles written for mathematics teachers. Yet the various issues involved sometimes seem so disparate that it is difficult to identify what the theme is about. Talking, reading, writing, using specialised terminology and symbolism, trying to understand mathematics in an unfamiliar language: these activities are all quite different linguistic aspects of learning mathematics.

Underlying all these matters is the need to communicate mathematics. Even 'communicate' is not quite the right word: it suggests the need for more than one person. What we have to do is to 'articulate' mathematical ideas, to find some satisfactory form in which these ideas can be expressed, whether for ourselves or for other people. Mathematics is concerned with patterns and structures, with properties and relationships, and these abstractions cannot be handled or handed over directly: they have to be expressed, recognised or applied in some tangible way.

Jaworski (1988) explains:

> As mathematics is not to be found just lying around to be picked up, a teacher has to find ways of making mathematical concepts available to pupils.

Jaworksi provides a constructivist view of mathematics teaching. Her concern is that pupils should be able to develop a coherent picture of what mathematics is about, in their own terms; and this picture may be different for everyone. In this constructivist view, language in all its forms has considerable importance, and yet direct transmission as a means of communicating mathematical knowledge is recognised as inadequate. Telling pupils something is rarely an effective way of ensuring that they learn and understand it.

Learning mathematics can be seen as a continuous process of making sense, not only of the subject itself, but of the quantitative and spatial aspects of reality. This process demands discussion and negotiation, it relies at times on skills of reading and writing, and ultimately it requires the development of formal language and notation in which abstractions can be made precise. The challenge for the mathematics teacher is to encourage a use of language in the classroom so as to provide a context within which pupils can make mathematical ideas their own.

Bibliography

Andrews, P. (1988) 'On assessment and teacher intervention', *Mathematics Teaching* 122.

Assessment of Performance Unit (APU) (1985) *A Review of Monitoring in Mathematics 1978 to 1982*, Parts 1 and 2, London, HMSO.

Association of Teachers of Mathematics (ATM) (various dates) *Points of Departure, 1, 2, 3, 4,* Derby, ATM.

ATM (1982) *Geometric Images* (and many more recent publications – see publicity material), Derby, ATM.

ATM (1984) *These have Worked for Us at A-level,* Derby, ATM.

ATM (1985) *These Have Also Worked for Us at A-level,* Derby, ATM.

ATM (1988) *Whatever Next?* Derby, ATM.

Austin, J.L. and Howson, A.G. (1979) 'Language and mathematical education', *Educational Studies in Mathematics* 10.

Aze, I. (1988) 'More on mental methods in mathematics', *Mathematics in School* 17.

Ball, D. (1988) 'Logplotter and other matters', *Micromath* 4 (3).

Ball, D. (1989) 'Software review: Numerator', *Micromath* 5 (1).

Barham, J. (1988) 'Deaf children and mathematics', *Struggle,* 21.

Bell, A.W., Costello, J. and Kuchemann, D.E. (1983) *A Review of Research in Mathematical Education,* Part A, Windsor, NFER-Nelson.

Bell, A.W., Swann, M. and Taylor, G. (1981) 'Choice of operations in verbal problems with decimal numbers', *Educational Studies in Mathematics* 12 (4).

Better Mathematics (1987) A Curriculum Development Study, London, HMSO.

Bolt, B. (1982) *Mathematical Activities,* Cambridge, Cambridge University Press.

Bolt, B. (1985) *More Mathematical Activities,* Cambridge, Cambridge University Press.

Bolt, B. (1987) *Even More Mathematical Activities,* Cambridge, Cambridge University Press.

Bowes, W., Sergeant, J, and Neave, E. (1988) 'Three points of view on mathematics teaching and support work', *Struggle* 21.

Briggs, L.J. (1970) *Handbook of Procedures for the Design of Instruction,* Pittsburgh, PA, American Institutes for Research.

Bunyard, D. (1989) 'Why microworlds?', Part 1, *Micromath* 5 (2).

Burkhardt, H. (1981) *The Real World and Mathematics,* Glasgow, Blackie.

Burrows, D. (1989) 'Opinion: the conversion', *Micromath* 5 (2).

Burton, L. (ed.) (1986) *Girls into Maths Can Go,* London, Holt, Rinehart & Winston.

Cockcroft, W.H. (1982) *Mathematics Counts,* London, DES/HMSO.

Cohen, L and Manion, L. (1989) *A Guide to Teaching Practice,* London, Routledge, third edition.

Craft, A. and Bardell, G. (eds) (1984) *Curriculum Opportunities in a Multicultural Society,* London, Harper & Row.

Csocsan, E. (1988) 'Problems of handicapped students', *Proceedings of the Sixth International Congress on Mathematical Education*, Budapest, Janos Bolyai Mathematical Society.
Davis, P.J. and Hersh, R. (1983) *The Mathematical Experience*, London, Penguin.
Denvir, B. (1988) What are we assessing in mathematics and what are we assessing for?, in D. Pimm (ed.) *Mathematics, Teachers and Children* London, Hodder & Stoughton.
Denvir, B., Stolz, C. and Brown, M. (1982) *Low Attainers in Mathematics 5–16*, London, Methuen Educational.
Dickson, L., Brown, M. and Gibson, O. (1984) *Children Learning Mathematics, a Teacher's Guide to Recent Research*, London, Holt, Rinehart & Winston.
Dobson, A. (1988) 'Software review: Tadpoles', *Micromath* 4 (2).
Drake, P. and Mardell, J. (1989) 'Beyond 16 – maths in the workplace', *Mathematics Teaching* 126.
Dunford, J. (1982) 'Games and recreations in the mathematics classroom', in M. Cornelius (ed.) *Teaching Mathematics*, Beckenham, Croom Helm.
Eagle, R. (1989) 'Centres of a triangle and a central dilemma', *Mathematics Teaching* 126.
Edmonds, B. and Ball, D. (1988) 'Looking for relevance – can we let them decide?', in D. Pimm (ed.) *Mathematics, Teachers and Children*, London, Hodder & Stoughton.
Educational Studies in Mathematics (1986) 17 (3): special issue on provision for gifted pupils.
Emblen, V. (1988) 'Asian children in schools', in D. Pimm (ed.) *Mathematics, Teachers and Children*, London, Hodder & Stoughton.
Ernest, P. (1986) 'Statistics and the media', *Mathematics in School* 15 (3).
Ernest, P. (1989) *Mathematics Teaching: the State of the Art*, London, Falmer Press.
Ernest, P. and Galvin, S. (1987) 'SMP 11–16 with low attainers', *Mathematics in School* 16 (5).
Fey, J.T. (1989) 'Technology and mathematics education', *Educational Studies in Mathematics* 20, 237–272.
Fielker, D. (1989) 'So what do we mean by "prediction"?' *Mathematics Teaching* 127.
Flegg, G. (1984) *Numbers – Their History and Meaning*, London, Penguin.
Fletcher, T. (1989) 'Trees', *Micromath* 5 (1).
Floyd, A. (1978) *Cognitive Development in the School Years*, Beckenham, Croom Helm.
Fowler, N. (1988) 'Open and closed affair', *Micromath* 4 (1).
Gailiunas, P. (1988) 'Numbers using Logo', *Micromath* 4 (3).
Gallimore, M. (1989) 'Graphwork – developing a pregression: introduction', *Teaching Statistics* 11 (1).
Gates, P. (1988) 'Working mathematically on circles and imagery', *Mathematics Teaching* 124.
Glenn, J.A. (1986) 'Mathematics international', *Mathematics in School* 15 (3).
Goodall, G. (1988) 'Spread at work', *Micromath* 4 (2).
Goodchild, S. (1988) 'School pupils' understanding of average', *Teaching Statistics* 19 (3).
Graham, J.D. (1977) 'Maths and CSE, Part 3', *Mathematics in School* 6 (5).
Green, D.R. (ed.) (1988) 'Information handling and statistics', *Teaching Statistics* 10 (1).
Grevsmuhl, U. (1988–9) 'Mathematics and modern art', series of articles in *Mathematics Teaching* 122–7.
Grugnetti, L. (1979) 'School mathematics makes Sardinians healthier', *Mathematics in School* 8 (5).
Harris, H. (1988) 'Common threads', *Mathematics Teaching* 123.
Hart, K. (1987) 'Children's mathematical frameworks, Part One: The volume of a cuboid is LxBxH', *Mathematics in School* 16 (3).
Hart, K. (1987) 'Children's mathematical frameworks, Part 3: Subtraction,' *Mathematics in School* 16 (5)
Hart, K. (1988) 'Children's mathematical frameworks – Part 4: The circumference of a circle,' *Mathematics in School* 17 (1)

Hart, K. Johnson, D.C., Brown, Dickson, L. and Clarkson, B. (1989) *Children's Mathematical Frameworks*: 8–13 Windsor, NFER-Nelson.

Head, J. (1981) 'Personality and the learning of mathematics,' *Educational Studies in Mathematics* 12 (3).

HMI (1977) *Gifted Children in Middle and Comprehensive Schools*, London DES/HMSO.

HMI (1979) *Aspects of Secondary Education in England*, London, DES/HMSO.

HMI (1989) *Aspects of Primary Education: The Teaching and Learning of Mathematics*, London, DES/HMSO.

Hoyles, C. (1982) 'The Pupil's view of mathematics learning', *Educational Studies in Mathematics* 13 (4).

Hytch, J.D. and Tidmarsh, D.E. (1969) 'Mathematics, streamed and non-streamed: a practical approach at the secondary stage', *Mathematics Teaching* 48.

Inner London Education Authority (ILEA) (1985) *Everyone Counts*, London, ILEA.

Isaacson, Z. (1987) *Teaching GCSE Mathematics*, London, Hodder & Stoughton.

Jaworski, B., (1988) '"Is" versus "seeing as" constructivism and the mathematics classroom', in D. Pimm (ed.) *Mathematics, Teachers and Children*, London, Hodder & Stoughton.

Jenkins, P. (1989) *Mrs Thatcher's Revolution*, London, Pan Books.

Jenner, H. (1988) 'Mathematics for a multicultural society', D. Pimm (ed.) *Mathematics, Teachers and Children*, London, Hodder & Stoughton.

Joffe, L. and Foxman, D. (1989) *Communicating Mathematical Ideas*, London, APU/HMSO.

Jones, D. (1988) 'Software review: Plan', *Micromath* 4 (1)

Jones, P.L. (1982) 'Learning mathematics in a second language, a problem with more and less', *Educational Studies in Mathematics* 13 (3).

Kennett, D. (1989) 'Using interactive video in secondary mathematics', in P. Ernest (ed.) *Mathematics Teaching: the State of the Art*, London, Falmer Press.

Kent Mathematics Project (KMP), London, Ward Lock Educational.

Kirkby, D. (1989) 'Maths games workshop – part 13: Types of mathematical games', *Mathematics in School* 18 (1).

Kitchen, A. (1989) 'Building a bridge between GCSE and A-level', *Mathematics in School* 18 (3).

Land, F. (1975) *The Language of Mathematics*, London, Murray, third edition.

Langdon, N. (1976) 'Smiling in the classroom', *Mathematics in School* 5 (5).

Larcombe, A. (1985) *Mathematical Learning Difficulties in the Secondary School*, Milton Keynes, Open University Press.

Lerman, S. (1989) 'Investigations, where to now?', P. Ernest (ed.) *Mathematics Teaching, the State of the Art*, London, Falmer Press.

Leron, U. (1988) 'Turtle programming,' *Micromath* 4 (3)

Logotron (undated) *The Logotron Logo Book*, Cambridge, Logotron.

Mathematical Association (undated) *Mathematics Homework on a Micro*, Leicester, Mathematical Association.

Mathematical Association (1923, 1938) *Reports on the Teaching of Geometry in Secondary Schools*, Leicester, Mathematical Association.

Mathematical Association (1985) *132 Short Programs for the Mathematics Classroom*, Leicester, Mathematical Association.

Mathematical Association (1988) *Mathematics in a Multicultural Society*, Leicester, Mathematical Association.

Mathematics Teaching (1986) 117, Special Edition – roots of mathematical activity.

Mathematics Teaching (1987) 121, Passages ' Three thirds of the way'.

Mathematics Teaching (1989) 126, Budapest 1988 (Collection of material).

Menninger, K. (1977) *Number Words and Number Symbols*, Boston, MA, MIT Press.

Micromath (1987) 3 (3) Autumn, Feature: Handling mathematical information.

Micromath (1989) 4 (1) Spring, Feature: Spreadsheets.
Morgan, C. (1989) 'A context for estimation', *Mathematics in School* 18 (3)
National Curriculum Council (1988) *Mathematics for Ages 5 to 16* (Proposals), London, DES/HMSO.
National Curriculum Council (1989) *Curriculum Guidance 2 – A Curriculum for All – Special Educational Needs in the National Curriculum*, London, DES/HMSO.
National Curriculum Council (1989) *Mathematics in the National Curriculum*, London DES/HMSO.
National Curriculum Council (1989) *Mathematics, Non-Statutory Guidance*, York, NCC.
National Curriculum Council (1989) *National Curriculum, from Policy to Practice*, London DES/HMSO.
National Curriculum Council (1989) *Science in the National Curriculum*, London, DES/HMSO.
Nicholson, A.R. (1977) 'Mathematics and language', *Mathematics in School* 6 (5).
Nicholson, A.R. (1980) 'Mathematical literacy', *Mathematics in School* 9 (2).
Nicholson, A.R. (1989) 'Mathematics and language revisited', *Mathematics in School* 18 (2)
Nolder, R.B. (1988) 'Responding to change', in D. Pimm (ed.) *Mathematics, Teachers and Children*, London, Hodder & Stoughton.
Nott, J. (1988) 'Mathematical development and children with visual impairment, *Struggle* 21.
Open University (1985) *Secondary Mathematics: Classroom Practice* (videotape).
Papert, S. (1980) *Mindstorms: Children Computers and Powerful Ideas*, Hemel Hempstead, Harvester Press.
Parr, A. (1988) 'Software review: Martello Tower', *Micromath* 4 (1).
Pask, G. (1976) 'Styles and strategies of learning', *British Journal of Educational Psychology* 46.
Pimm, D. (1987) *Speaking Mathematically*, London Routledge.
Pirie, S. (1987) *Mathematics Investigations in Your Classroom*, London, Macmillan.
Pirie, S. (1989) 'Classroom-based assessment', in P. Ernest (ed.) *Mathematics Teaching, the State of the Art*, London, Falmer Press.
Pirie, S. and Schwarzenberger, R. (1988) 'It's what you say and what you do', *Mathematics Teaching* 123.
Plunkett, S. (1979) 'Decomposition and all that rot', *Mathematics in School* 8 (3).
Price, M. and Price, S. (1988) 'Micro magic squares', *Micromath* 4 (3).
Radatz, H. (1979) 'Some aspects of individual differences in mathematics education', *Journal of Research in Mathematical Education* 10.
Rahman, D. (1988) 'Software review: Pyxidium', *Micromath* 4 (2).
Rahman, R. (1988) 'Logo in the classroom', *Micromath* 4 (3).
Romiszowski, A.J. (1979) 'What's happening to individualised mathematics?', *Programmed Learning and Educational Technology* 16 (2).
Rouncefield, M. (1989) 'Practical statistics in the sixth form', *Mathematics in School* 18 (1)
Schools Examinations and Assessment Council (SEAC) (1990) *A Guide to Teacher Assessment, Pack C: A Source Book of Teacher Assessment*, Oxford, Heinemann Educational.
School Mathematics Project (SMP) (1965, metric edition 1969) *SMP Book 1*, Cambridge, Cambridge University Press.
SMP 11–16 (School Mathematics Project), Cambridge, Cambridge University Press.
SMILE (Secondary Mathematics Individualised Learning Experiment), ILEA.
Selkirk, K.E. (1982) *Pattern and Place*, Cambridge, Cambridge University Press.
Shuard, H. and Rothery, A. (1984) *Children Reading Mathematics*, London, Murray.
Skemp. R.R. (1976) 'Relational understanding and instrumental understanding', *Mathematics Teaching* 77.
Smith, D. (1987) 'It's not what you say, it's the way that you do it', *Mathematics Teaching* 121.

Spender, D. and Sarah, E. (eds) (1981) *Learning to Lose*, London, Women's Press.
Steel, B.M. (1988) 'What if we cannot see?', *Struggle* 21.
Straker, A. (1983) *Mathematics for Gifted Pupils*, Harlow, Longman/Schools Council.
Szendrei, J. (1989) 'Parallels: teaching statistics', *Mathematics Teaching* 128.
Tall, D.O. (1986) *Graphic Calculus 1, 11 and 111*, Barnet, Glentop Publishers.
Tall, D.O. (1987) 'Whither calculus?', *Mathematics Teaching* 118.
Tarquin Publications (Diss, Norfolk) 1985–9) *Make Shapes 1,2,3, Mathematics Curiosities 1, 2, 3*, and other publications.
Thomas, B. and Costello, J. (1988) 'Identifying children's attitudes to mathematics', *Mathematics Teaching* 122.
Townsend, R.. (1987) 'Is a maze a prison?', *Micromath* 3 (2).
Trickett, L. and Sulke, F. (1988) 'Low attainers can do mathematics', in D. Pimm (ed.) *Mathematics, Teachers and Children*, London, Hodder & Stoughton.
Tytherleigh, B. and Watson, A. (1987) 'Mathematics and dance', *Mathematics Teaching* 121.
Van Dormolen, J. (1977) 'Learning to understand what giving a proof really means', *Educational Studies in Mathematics* 8 (1).
Watson, A. (1988) 'Cut my cote', *Mathematics Teaching* 122.
Watts, W.J. (1979) 'Some problems in teaching mathematics to deaf children', *Journal of the British Association of Teachers of the Deaf* 3 (1)
Williams, J. (1989) 'Modelling real data', *Micromath* 5 (1).
Witkin, H.A., Moore, C.A., Goodenough, D.R.and Cox, P.W. 'Field-dependent and field-independent cognitive styles and their educational implications', *Review of Educational Research* 47.
Woodrow, D. (1984) 'Some cultural impacts on children learning mathematics', *Mathematics in School* 13 (5).
Woodrow, D. (1989) 'Multicultural and anti-racist mathematics teaching', in P. Ernest (ed.) *Mathematics Teaching – the State of the Art* London, Falmer Press.
Woods, M. (1988) 'Real problem solving in a special school', *Mathematics in School* 17 (4).
Zaslavsky, C. (1973) *Africa Counts*, Boston, MA, Prindle, Weber and Schmidt.
Zepp, R.A. (1981) 'Relationships, between mathematics achievement and various English language proficiencies', *Educational Studies in Mathematics* 12 (1).
Zepp, R.A. (1982) 'Bilingual's understanding of logical connectives in English and Sesotho', *Educational Studies in Mathematics* 13 (2).

SOURCES OF QUOTED SOFTWARE AND USEFUL ADDRESSES

Association of Teachers of Mathematics (ATM)
7 Shaftesbury Street
Derby DE3 8YB

GEM Software
13 Trinity Close
Balsham
Cambridge CB1 6DW

Logotron
Dales Brewery
Gwydir Street
Cambridge CB1 2LJ

Mathematical Association
259 London Road
Leicester LE2 3BE

MEP – for MEP material contact:
The Advisory Unit
Endymion Road
Hatfield
Herts AL10 8AU

MESU – for MESU material contact:
NCET
Science Park
University of Warwick
Coventry CV4 7EZ

PEG Exeter
School of Education
St Lukes
Exeter EX1 2LV

Shell Centre for Mathematical Education
The University
Notthingham NG7 2RD

SMILE – for SMILE material contact:
ILECC
John Ruskin Street
London SE5 OPQ

Anita Straker
Mundays
St Mary Bourne
Andover
Hants SP1 6AY

Index